KS3 Success

Workbook

Mathematics
SATs
Levels 3-6

Fiona Mapp

Contents

Number

Algebra

Shape, space & measures

Handling data

Homework diary

TOPIC	STUDY DATE	SCORE
Numbers 1		/28
Numbers 2		/33
Positive & negative numbers		/36
Working with numbers		/41
Fractions		/41
Decimals		/36
Percentages		/32
Equivalents of using a calculator		/32
Rounding		/41
Estimates & checking calculations		/24
Ratio		/29
Algebra 1		/31
Algebra 2		/34
Equations 1		/43
Equations 2		/23
Numbers patterns & sequences		/30
Coordinates & graphs		/27
More graphs		/24
Using linear graphs		/16
Shapes		/28
Solids		/19
Symmetry		/25
Construction and LOGO		/18
Angles & tessellations		/27
Bearings & scale drawings		/28
Transformations		/18
Measures & measurement 1		/28
Measures & measurement 2		/24
Area & perimeter of 2D shapes		/25
Volume of 3D solids		/20
Collecting data		/21
Representing information		/17
Scatter diagrams & misleading graphs		/15
Averages 1		/22
Averages 2		/22
Probability 1		/23
Probability 2		/18

Progress plotter

Once you have completed a Unit, and filled in your score on the Homework Diary opposite, use this progress plotter to chart your success! Fill in the boxes with your score for each unit and watch your results get better and better.

	Nearly all right – Excellent work!	More than half – Good but keep trying.	Less than half – Room for improvement.	Under 5 – Needs more work.
Numbers 1				
Numbers 2				
Positive & negative numbers				
Working with numbers				
Fractions				
Decimals				
Percentages				
Equivalents & using a calculator				
Rounding				
Estimates & checking calculations				
Ratio				
Algebra 1				
Algebra 2				
Equations 1				
Equations 2				
Number patterns & sequences				
Coordinates & graphs				
More graphs				
Using linear graphs				
Shapes				
Solids				
Symmetry				
Construction and LOGO				
Angles & tessellations				
Bearings & scale drawings				
Transformations				
Measures & measurement 1				
Measures & measurement 2				
Area & perimeter of 2D shapes				
Volume of 3D solids				
Collecting data				
Representing information				
Scatter diagrams & misleading graphs				
Averages 1				
Averages 2				
Probability 1				
Probability 2				

Numbers 1

A

Choose just one answer, a, b, c or d.

1 Which of these is the smallest number? **2406, 75, 705, 82** (1 mark)

a) 2406 ☐   b) 75 ☑

c) 705 ☐   d) 82 ☐

2 The digit 5 in the number 25712 stands for: (1 mark)

a) units ☐   b) tens ☐

c) thousands ☑   d) ten thousands ☐

3 Which number represents sixty-four thousand three hundred and two? (1 mark)

a) 64 320 ☐   b) 64 302 ☑

c) 6432 ☐   d) 64 000 302 ☐

4 What is the fourth multiple of 6? (1 mark)

a) 6 ☐ b) 12 ☐ c) 18 ☐ d) 24 ☑

5 Here are some cards: [2] [7] [3] [8]

What is the largest number you can make with these cards? (1 mark)

a) 8372 ☐   b) 8327 ☐

c) 8732 ☑   d) 8723 ☐

6 Here are some cards: [3] [4] [1] [2]

Which of the following is the smallest even number you can make with these cards? (1 mark)

a) 1432 ☐   b) 1234 ☑

c) 1423 ☐   d) 4231 ☐   Score 6/6

B

Answer all parts of all questions.

1 Write the following numbers in words.

a) 403 ....

b) 3627 .... (2 marks)

2 Write down the following numbers in figures.

a) Six hundred and forty-five .... 645 .... (1 mark)

b) Two million, three hundred and four ...... 2,000,304 .... (1 mark)

3 What value does the digit 6 represent in each of these numbers?

a) 562 .... 60 .... Tens .... (1 mark)

b) 2716 .... 6 .... Units .... (1 mark)

c) 627 143 .... 600,000 .... (1 mark)

4 Afshan has some cards: [7] [1] [4] [3]

Use these cards to make:

a) the largest number possible .... 7431 .... (1 mark)

b) a number that is smaller than 7143 .... 4317 .... (1 mark)

c) the smallest possible even number .... 1347 .... (1 mark)

5 Arrange these numbers in order of size, smallest first.

a) 64, 3702, 1462, 1731, 421, 506 ...... 64 421 506 1462 1731 3702 ...... (2 marks)

b) 275, 1362, 2701, 846, 2, 27 ...... 2 27 275 846 1362 2701 ...... (2 marks)

Score /14

C These are SATs-style questions. Answer all parts of the questions.

1 a) Josh lives at number seventy-eight Sycamore Road. Three of Josh's friends live in Sycamore Road. Write down the house numbers.

Hannah

78

I Live at four hundred and six.

....406....

Matthew

I Live at ninety-five.

....95....

I Live at one hundred and sixty-nine.

169

Robert

(3 marks)

b) Write the numbers of the four houses in order, smallest first.

....78...., ...95...., ...169...., ...406.... (2 marks)

2 Here are some cards: 2   3   7   1   6

a) Using the cards above, write down the largest number possible.

....7 6 3 2 1.... (1 mark)

b) Write down the smallest possible even number when using all the cards.

....1 2 3 6 7.... (1 mark)

3 Write a number that is bigger than two thousand but smaller than two thousand two hundred.

....2150.... (1 mark)

Score   / 8

Total score   / 28

How well did you do? ✗ 1–6 **Try again**   7–13 **Getting there**   14–20 **Good work**   21–28 **Excellent!** ✓

For more help on this topic see KS3 Maths 3–6 Success Guide pages 4–5.

Numbers 2

A

Choose just one answer, a, b, c or d.

1 Look at this list of numbers: 4, 7, 9, 20.
Which one is a prime number? (1 mark)

a) 7 ☑   b) 4 ☐   c) 9 ☐   d) 20 ☐

2 What is the positive square root of 64? (1 mark)

a) 7 ☐   b) –8 ☐   c) –7 ☐   d) 8 ☑

3 Work out the lowest common multiple of 6 and 8. (1 mark)

a) 48 ☐   b) 3 ☐   c) 24 ☐   d) 2 ☐

4 What is the value of 3^3? (1 mark)

a) 9 ☐   b) 12 ☐   c) 72 ☐   d) 27 ☐

5 What is the reciprocal of $\frac{7}{9}$? (1 mark)

a) $\frac{9}{7}$ ☐   b) $\frac{7}{9}$ ☐   c) $\frac{9}{5}$ ☐   d) 9 ☐

6 Which one of these numbers is a factor of 12? (1 mark)

a) 36 ☐   b) 6 ☐   c) 18 ☐   d) 24 ☐

Score   / 6

B

Answer all parts of all questions.

1 Some numbers are in the cloud.

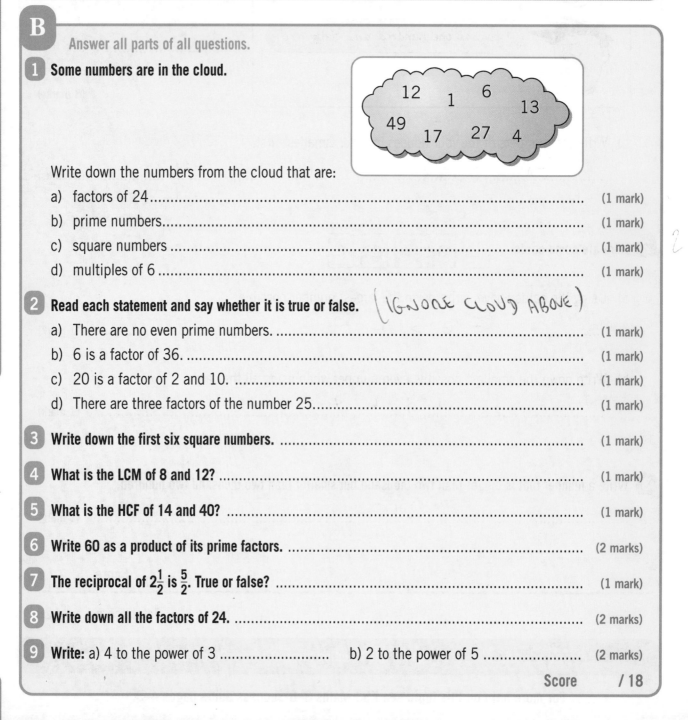

Write down the numbers from the cloud that are:

a) factors of 24 .... (1 mark)

b) prime numbers .... (1 mark)

c) square numbers .... (1 mark)

d) multiples of 6 .... (1 mark)

2 Read each statement and say whether it is true or false. *(IGNORE CLOUD ABOVE)*

a) There are no even prime numbers. .... (1 mark)

b) 6 is a factor of 36. .... (1 mark)

c) 20 is a factor of 2 and 10. .... (1 mark)

d) There are three factors of the number 25 .... (1 mark)

3 Write down the first six square numbers. .... (1 mark)

4 What is the LCM of 8 and 12? .... (1 mark)

5 What is the HCF of 14 and 40? .... (1 mark)

6 Write 60 as a product of its prime factors. .... (2 marks)

7 The reciprocal of $2\frac{1}{2}$ is $\frac{5}{2}$. True or false? .... (1 mark)

8 Write down all the factors of 24. .... (2 marks)

9 Write: a) 4 to the power of 3 .... b) 2 to the power of 5 .... (2 marks)

Score   / 18

These are SATs-style questions. Answer all parts of the questions.

1 **William has 12 counters. He can put them in 3 rows, with 4 counters in each row.**

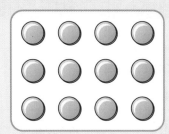

   a) Draw a diagram to show how he can put 12 counters in 2 rows, with the same number of counters in each row.

                                        (1 mark)

   b) Draw a diagram to show a different way that William can put 12 counters in a different number of rows, with the same number of counters in each row.

                                        (1 mark)

   c) Fill in the table to show how many rows William can make with 12 counters, and how many counters there are in each row.

Number of rows	Number of counters in each row
1 row	12 counters in each row
.... rows	.... counters in each row
3 rows	.... counters in each row
.... rows	.... counters in each row
.... rows	.... counters in each row
.... rows	1 counter in each row

                                        (4 marks)

   d) William says: *I can put 12 counters in 5 rows with the same number of counters in each row.*

      Explain why William is wrong. .... (1 mark)

2 **Penelope and Tom are describing some numbers. Decide which number each is thinking about.**

Penelope   *My number is a square number, greater than 10 and less than 20.*

Tom   *My number is the only even prime number.*

Penelope's number is ....

Tom's number is ....   (2 marks)

                                        Score   **/ 9**

Total score   **/ 33**

How well did you do?   ✗ 1–8 Try again   9–16 Getting there   17–24 Good work   25–33 Excellent! ✓

For more help on this topic see KS3 Maths 3–6 Success Guide pages 6–7.

9

Positive & negative numbers

A

Answer all parts of all questions.

1 **Look at these signs:**

> is greater than   = is equal to   < is less than

Fill in each gap with one of these signs to make each of the statements true.

a) –3 6   b) –4 .... –10   c) 7 .... –6   d) 0 .... –3   (4 marks)

2 **Here are some number cards:**

a) Choose two cards that add up to give –10. .... (1 mark)

b) Choose two cards that add up to give –7. .... (1 mark)

c) Choose two cards that multiply to give –15. .... (1 mark)

3 **Each of the calculations below has an answer that is one of the numbers from this list:**

   12, –12, –3, –4, 3, 8.

Select the correct number for each answer.

a) –3 × –4 = ...   b) –16 ÷ (–2) = ...

c) 8 – (–4) = ...   d) 4 + (–7) = ...

e) –9 ÷ (–3) = ...   f) –7 – (–3) = ...   (6 marks)

4 **Work out the following:**

a) –7 × –3 = ...   b) –9 – (–4) = ...

c) 12 ÷ (–6) = ...   d) –8 × 2 = ...   (4 marks)

5 **The temperature at midday was –12°C. By midnight it had dropped by 10 degrees.**
What was the temperature at midnight?

.... (1 mark)

6 **Here are some numbers in a number pyramid.**
The number in each rectangle is found
by adding the two numbers below.

Complete the number pyramid.   (2 marks)

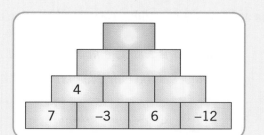

7 **Here are some signs:**

Insert the correct sign to make each calculation correct.

a) –12 .... –3 = 4   b) –7 .... –3 = –4

c) 9 .... –3 = –3   d) 12 .... –5 = 7   (4 marks)

Score   / 24

10

B

These are SATs-style questions. Answer all parts of the questions.

1 **The arrow on the thermometer shows a temperature of 20°C.**

a) Draw an arrow on the thermometer to show a temperature of 32°C.
Label the arrow 32°C.   (1 mark)

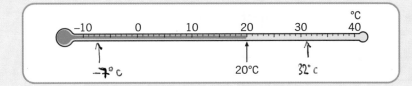

b) Draw an arrow on the thermometer to show a temperature of –7°C.   (2 marks)

c) The temperature was 25°C. It fell by 27 degrees.

What is the temperature now?.. (1 mark)

d) The temperature was –9°C. It rose by 21 degrees.

What is the temperature now? .... (1 mark)

e) Write these temperatures in order, highest first.

–6°C, 9°C, –3°C, 15°C, 0°C, –12°C

...............°C, ...°C, ...°C, ...°C, ...°C, ...°C
highest   lowest

(1 mark)

2 **Here is a list of numbers:**

–9, –5, –1, 0, 3, 2, 5

Choose a number from the list to make each statement correct.

a) 3 – .... = 4   b) 5 × .... = –25

c) –9 + ... = –4   d) 2 – .... = 7

e) –9 ÷ .... = –3   (5 marks)

f) What is the total of all seven numbers in the list?   (1 mark)

Score   / 12

Total score   / 36

How well did you do?   ✗ 1–6 **Try again**   7–15 **Getting there**   16–26 **Good work**   27–36 **Excellent!** ✓

For more help on this topic see KS3 Maths 3–6 Success Guide pages 8–9.

11

POSITIVE & NEGATIVE NUMBERS   Number

Working with numbers

A   Answer all parts of all questions.

1 Match each of the calculations with the correct answer.

15 × 10	15
15 × 100	15 000
15 × 1000	1 500 000
30 × 5000	1500
3 × 50	150
300 × 5000	150 000
1.5 × 10	

(4 marks)   4

2 Carry out the following divisions.

a) 2700 ÷ 90 = ...   b) 5000 ÷ 100 = ...   c) 650 ÷ 50 = ...   (3 marks)   3

3 Complete the magic square, so that the numbers along the horizontal, vertical and diagonal add up to the same value.

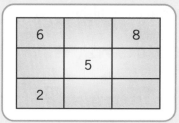

(2 marks)   2

4 Work out the following calculations.

a) 273 + 496 = ...   b) 972 − 631 = ...

c) 2718 × 4 = ...   d) 411 ÷ 3 = ...   (4 marks)   )

5 Work out the following calculations, showing all your working.

a) 279 × 42   b) 6305 × 84   c) 1665 ÷ 37   d) 4648 ÷ 56   (4 marks)   4

6 A bar of chocolate costs 72 pence. How much would 37 bars cost? .... (1 mark)

7 A school hall has 1596 chairs in it.

The chairs are placed in rows and there are 38 chairs in each row.

How many rows are there? .... (1 mark)

8 A shop buys 126 sweaters.

If each sweater is sold for £65, how much money does the shop take in total?

.... (2 marks)   2

Score   / 22

B

These are SATs-style questions. Answer all parts of the questions.

1 **Fill in the missing numbers:**

a) 872 – .... = 694

b) .... – 412 = 873

c) 27 × .... = 108

d) .... ÷ 22 = 396   (4 marks)   4

2 **There are 45 pencils in a box.**
A box of pencils costs £3.50.

a) How many pencils are there in 6 boxes?   .... pencils   (1 mark)

b) How much do 7 boxes cost?   £ ....   (1 mark)

c) How much do 135 pencils cost?   £ ....   (1 mark)

d) How many boxes of pencils can be bought with £42?   .... boxes   (1 mark)

3 **Fill in the missing numbers so**
that the answer is always 60.

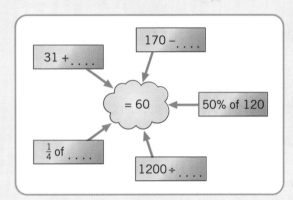

(4 marks)   4

4 **Nigel owns a garden centre. He sells small shrubs for £6.75 each.**

a) Nigel sells 37 small shrubs one weekend to Mrs Robinson.
How much does he get for the 37 shrubs?   £ ....   (2 marks)   2

b) Each small shrub needs 60 grams of compost when it is planted.
Mrs Robinson buys a sack of compost weighing 2000 grams.

i)   How many shrubs can be planted?   .... shrubs   (2 marks)   2

ii) How much more compost does she need in order to
plant all 37 shrubs?   .... grams   (1 mark)

5 **Raj puts a three-digit whole number into his calculator.**
He multiplies it by 10.

a) Fill in one other digit that you know
must be on the calculator display.

(1 mark)

b) Raj starts again with the same three-digit
number. This time he multiplies it by 1000.
Fill in all the digits that might be on the
calculator display.

(1 mark)

Score   / 19

Total score   / 41

How well did you do?   ✗ 1–9 **Try again**   10–19 **Getting there**   20–32 **Good work**   33–41 **Excellent!** ✓

For more help on this topic see KS3 Maths 3–6 Succe1ss Guide pages 10–11.

13

Fractions

A

Answer all parts of all questions.

1 Look at these diagrams. What fractions have been shaded?   (3 marks)

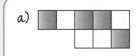
a)

b)

c)

Fraction shaded ..$\frac{1}{2}$..   Fraction shaded ....   Fraction shaded ....

2 Fill in the blanks in these equivalent fractions.

a) $\frac{2}{9} = \frac{6}{27}$ b) $\frac{3}{5} = \frac{15}{25}$ c) $\frac{27}{99} = \frac{9}{33} = \frac{3}{.....}$ d) $\frac{10}{17} = \frac{30}{.....}$ (4 marks)

3 Reduce these fractions to their lowest terms.

a) $\frac{2}{8} =$ ....   b) $\frac{4}{20} =$ ....   c) $\frac{6}{12} =$ ....   d) $\frac{25}{35} =$ ....   (4 marks)

4 Change these improper fractions to mixed numbers.

a) $\frac{7}{2} =$ ....   b) $\frac{4}{3} =$ ....   c) $\frac{5}{3} =$ ....   d) $\frac{10}{4} = =$ ....   (4 marks)

5 Work out the following: a) $\frac{2}{7} + \frac{3}{5} =$ ....   b) $\frac{8}{13} - \frac{1}{2} =$ ....   (2 marks)

Arrange these fractions in order of size, smallest first.

6 a) $\frac{4}{5}, \frac{1}{3}, \frac{2}{9}, \frac{4}{7}, \frac{1}{2}$ ....   b) $\frac{9}{13}, \frac{3}{5}, \frac{2}{7}, \frac{1}{3}$ ....   (2 marks)

7 Work out the following: a) $\frac{2}{7} \times \frac{4}{9} =$ ....   b) $\frac{6}{7} \div \frac{3}{14} =$ ....   (2 marks)

8 Work out the amounts in each statement and decide whether the statement is true or false.

a) $\frac{3}{5}$ of 20 is greater than $\frac{2}{7}$ of 14. ....   (1 mark)

b) $\frac{9}{11}$ of 44 is smaller than $\frac{1}{3}$ of 72. ....   (1 mark)

c) $\frac{2}{7}$ of 21 is greater than $\frac{3}{5}$ of 15. ....   (1 mark)

d) $\frac{1}{3}$ of 27 is smaller than $\frac{5}{9}$ of 45. ....   (1 mark)

9 Mark has a fruit stall. $\frac{2}{7}$ of the fruit he has are apples.

If he has 245 pieces of fruit in total, how many are apples? ....   (1 mark)

10 A hospital has 350 pints of milk delivered.

If $\frac{2}{5}$ of the milk is skimmed, how many pints are not skimmed? ....   (1 mark)

Score   / 27

B

1 **Rani and David bake some cakes. They have 16 cakes each.**

a) Rani eats a quarter of her cakes.
How many cakes does Rani eat? .... (1 mark)

b) David eats 12 of his 16 cakes.
What fraction of his cakes does David eat?.. (1 mark)

c) How many cakes are left altogether? .... (1 mark)

2 **Fill in the missing values so that the answer is always 8.**

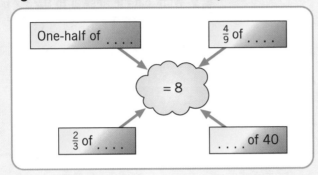

(4 marks)

3 **Carry out these calculations.**

a) $\frac{1}{2}$ of £60 = ... (1 mark)

b) $\frac{2}{3}$ of £900 = ... (1 mark)

c) $\frac{2}{7} + \frac{3}{5}$ = ... (1 mark)

d) $\frac{4}{7} \times \frac{2}{5}$ = ... (1 mark)

4 **In a book there are three pictures on the same page.**

Picture 1 uses $\frac{1}{4}$ of the page.

Picture 2 uses $\frac{1}{16}$ of the page.

Picture 3 uses $\frac{1}{64}$ of the page.

a) In total, what fraction of the page do pictures 1 and 2 make up? .... (2 marks)

b) To put a picture in a book
is more expensive than
text.

Cost of picture = £35 for every $\frac{1}{8}$ of a page

If a picture takes up $\frac{3}{32}$ of
a page, how much
will it cost? .... (1 mark)

Score   / 14

Total score   / 41

How well did you do? ✗ 1–9 **Try again**   10–19 **Getting there**   20–32 **Good work**   33–41 **Excellent!** ✓

For more help on this topic see KS3 Maths 3–6 Success Guide pages 12–13.

15

FRACTIONS   Number

Decimals

A

Choose just one answer, a, b, c or d.

1 Here are some number cards: (1 mark)

| 6.27 | 6.31 | 6.21 | 6.205 |

Which of these cards has the smallest number?

a) 6.205 ☐   b) 6.31 ☐
c) 6.27 ☐   d) 6.21 ☐

2 Work out the answer to 4.29 + 6.14. (1 mark)

a) 11.43 ☐   b) 10.29 ☐
c) 10.42 ☐   d) 10.43 ☐

3 Work out the answer to 12.62 − 9.71. (1 mark)

a) 2.91 ☐   b) 3.11 ☐
c) 3.01 ☐   d) 2.94 ☐

4 Work out the answer to 9.23 × 6. (1 mark)

a) 55.83 ☐   b) 54.83 ☐
c) 54.38 ☐   d) 55.38 ☐

Score   / 4

B

Answer all parts of all questions.

1 Here is a decimal: 5.24. The 2 in this number has a value of two tenths.
For each of these decimals, write the place value of the number 6.

a) 14.026 ....   b) 7.61 ....
c) 56.123 ....   d) 8.162 ....   (4 marks)

2 Look at each of these statements and state whether it is true or false.

a) 0.25 is bigger than 0.19. .... (1 mark)
b) 0.72 is smaller than 0.721. .... (1 mark)
c) 0.639 is smaller than 0.6385. .... (1 mark)
d) 2.79 is bigger than 2.789. .... (1 mark)

3 Here are some numbers: 4.39, 3.69, 3.691, 2.71, 4.385, 3.62, 4.38.
Arrange these numbers in order of size, smallest first.

.... (2 marks)

4 Each number in the number pyramid is found by
adding the two numbers immediately below it, e.g.
Complete the larger pyramid: (4 marks)

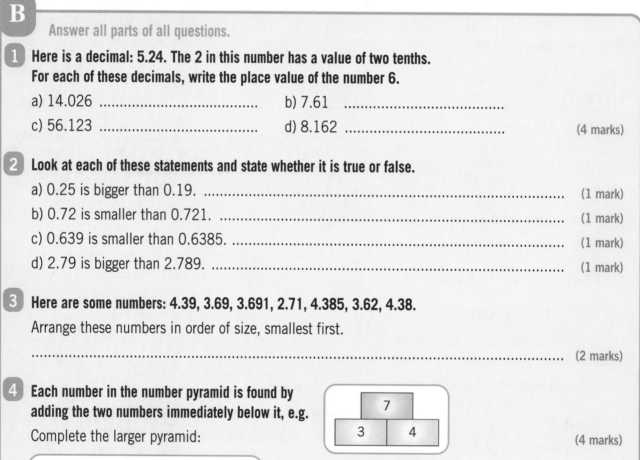

5 Four friends are playing a game. Their scores are shown below:

Tom	Ahmed	Rebecca	Lin
6.27	4.98	5.07	5.065

   a) Who won the game, with the highest score? .... (1 mark)

   b) What is the difference between Ahmed's and Lin's scores? .... (1 mark)

6 A CD costs £11.58. James buys six copies. How much must he pay for the six CDs?

.... (1 mark)

7 Here are some number cards:

Fill in each of the gaps using one of the number cards, to make the statements correct.

   a) 1.4 × .... = 14   b) 22.6 × .... = 2260

   c) 5.9 ÷ .... = 0.59   d) 14.73 ÷ .... = 0.01473

   e) 275 ÷ .... = 0.275   f) 37.6 × .... = 37 600   (6 marks)

Score   / 23

C

These are SATs-style questions. Answer all parts of the questions.

1 Complete these calculations to make them correct.

   a) 14.6 + 3.9 = 12.1 + ... (1 mark)

   b) 8.3 × 4 = 2 × .... (1 mark)

   c) 937.65 − 2.3 = 654.1 + ... (1 mark)

   d) 124.8 ÷ 4 = 2 × .... (1 mark)

2 Look at these number cards:

3.1   10   100   2.7   4.6   1000   3.05

   a) Choose two of these cards to make the smallest possible answer.

      ☐ × ☐ = ... (1 mark)

   b) Choose two of the cards to make the answer 3050.

      ☐ × ☐ = 3050 (2 marks)

   c) Choose two of the cards to give the answer 0.046.

      ☐ × ☐ = 0.046 (2 marks)

Score   / 9

Total score   / 36

How well did you do?   ✗ 1–10 **Try again**   11–19 **Getting there**   20–27 **Good work**   28–36 **Excellent!** ✓

For more help on this topic see KS3 Maths 3–6 Success Guide pages 14–15.

Percentages

A

Answer all parts of all questions.

1 Here are some statements about a hospital. Fill in the missing percentages to make the statements correct.

a) 73% of the nurses are females, which means ....% are not females.   (1 mark)

b) 62% of the patients stay in hospital for 3 or more days, which means ....%
of the patients stay in hospital less than 3 days.   (1 mark)

2 The building society has reported a 10% rise in house prices over the last year.
If the average price of a house last year was £90 000, what is the average house price this year?   (2 marks)

3 A shoe shop is having a sale:

Shoe World
15% off
marked prices

A pair of trainers originally cost £130.

What is the sale price of the trainers? ....   (2 marks)

4 Match the calculations with the correct answers. The first one has been done for you.

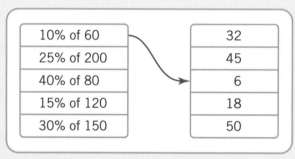

10% of 60		32
25% of 200		45
40% of 80		6
15% of 120		18
30% of 150		50

(4 marks)

5 A train ticket from Manchester to Birmingham costs £24 return. If you book in advance, the price of the
ticket is reduced by 6%. What is the advanced booking price of the ticket? ....   (1 mark)

6 These are some of the results for Hywel's end of year examinations:

Maths   64 out of 80   = ...%   English   27 out of 50   = ...%

German   42 out of 110 = ...%   Science   121 out of 150 = ...%

a) Change each of the results into a percentage. ....   (2 marks)

b) In which subject did Hywel do worst? ....   (1 mark)

7 A survey showed the favourite flavours of crisps, chosen by 500 people were as follows:

        Salt 'n' vinegar 204   Cheese 'n' onion 196   Beef 100

a) What percentage preferred cheese 'n' onion flavoured crisps? ....%   (2 marks)

b) What percentage of people did not choose beef flavour? ....%   (2 marks)

Score   / 18

Ⓒ Indicates that a calculator may be used

B

These are SATs-style questions. Answer all parts of the questions.

1 Work out the missing numbers.

C a) 15% of 40 grams = ...grams   (1 mark)

b) £9.75 = 15% of £..   (1 mark)

c) £30 = 20% of £...   (1 mark)

d) 45% of 620 litres = ...litres   (1 mark)

2 A cake shop sells some different types of cakes.

C The table shows how many cakes they sold in one day.

Cake	Number of cakes sold	Takings (£)
Doughnut	146	32.12
Battenberg	45	8.10
Coconut slice	37	20.35
Almond slice	48	41.76
Chocolate brownie	74	70.30
Total	350	172.63

a) What percentage of the total number of cakes sold were doughnuts?

Show your working. ....% (2 marks)

b) What percentage of the total takings was for doughnuts?

Show your working. ....% (2 marks)

c) What percentage of the total number of cakes sold were Battenberg?

Show your working. ....% (2 marks)

3 Calculate:

C a) i) 4% of £32.50 = £...   (1 mark)

ii) $12\frac{1}{2}$% of £78 = £...   (1 mark)

b) A television costs £199. In a sale, 28% is taken off the price. Work out the sale price
of the television set.

£ ....   (2 marks)

Score   / 14

Total score   / 32

How well did you do?   ✗ 1–7 **Try again**   8–14 **Getting there**   15–22 **Good work**   23–32 **Excellent!** ✓

For more help on this topic see KS3 Maths 3–6 Success Guide pages 16–17.

Equivalents & using a calculator

A

Answer all parts of all questions.

1 Change these fractions into decimals and percentages.

a) Fraction = $\frac{3}{5}$ decimal = ...   percentage = ...% (2 marks) 2

b) Fraction = $\frac{1}{8}$ decimal = ...   percentage = ...% (2 marks) 2

2 Complete each of these statements by writing a fraction, decimal or percentage to make each one correct.

a) $\frac{1}{4}$ and 25% are the same as the decimal .... (1 mark) (

b) 30% and 0.3 are the same as the fraction .... (1 mark) (

c) $\frac{1}{8}$ and 0.125 are the same as the percentage .... (1 mark) (

3 Here are some cards:

| $\frac{2}{5}$ | 72% | $\frac{3}{8}$ | 25% | 0.9 | 0.41 | 30% |

Put these cards in order of size, smallest first. .... (2 marks) 2

4 **C** The same television is being sold in different shops.

SUPERS	**Electricals**	**RAMONES**
$\frac{1}{3}$ off	20% off	TV £375
TV £570	TV £510	plus VAT at 17.5%

Work out the price of the television in each of the three shops.

SUPERS £................,   ELECTRICALS £................,   RAMONES £................ (3 marks) 3

Which shop sells the television at the cheapest price? .... (1 mark) 1

5 Siân and Robert are looking at a shape.

30% is shaded

$\frac{3}{10}$ is shaded

Could they both be right? Why? .... (2 marks) 2

6 Work out these calculations without using a calculator:

a) $5 + 3 \times 2 =$

b) $(6 + 3) \times 4 =$

c) $12 + 6 \div 2 =$ (3 marks) 2

7 **C** Use a calculator to work out these calculations.

a) $\dfrac{6.2 + 4.9}{3.7 \times 4.1} =$ .... b) $\dfrac{\sqrt{10.3} - 2.1}{(2.3)^2} =$ .... c) $\dfrac{9.3^2 \times 2}{\sqrt{5.6}} = =$ .... (3 marks) 3

Score   / 21

C *Indicates that a calculator may be used*

B

These are SATs-style questions. Answer all parts of the questions.

1 Charlotte has some cards:

| 0.125 | 0.75 | $\frac{1}{2}$ | 0.4 | 40% | 50% |

Reece has some different cards:

| $\frac{2}{5}$ | 0.5 | 75% | $\frac{1}{8}$ | $\frac{15}{20}$ | 12.5% |

They decide to group the cards together, so that the cards in each group are equivalent.
Complete the groups of cards below:

$\frac{2}{5}$, ..., ..., 0.5, ..., ..., 12.5%   ...., 0.75, ...   (4 marks)

2 A target board has some fractions, decimals and percentages:

0.55	$\frac{1}{25}$	$\frac{1}{3}$	$\frac{11}{20}$	$\frac{2}{7}$
$\frac{3}{8}$	20%	0.9	0.375	$\frac{1}{20}$
90%	$0.\dot{3}$	0.05	$\frac{2}{10}$	$\frac{9}{10}$
0.2	5%	37.5%	$33.\dot{3}\%$	55%

Here are some of the sets which are equivalent:

Set 1   55%,   0.55, $\frac{11}{20}$ Set 2   20%,   0.2, $\frac{2}{10}$

There are four other sets which are equivalent. Write them in the spaces provided.

Set 3   ...., ..., ...   (1 mark)

Set 4   ...., ..., ...   (1 mark)

Set 5   ...., ..., ...   (1 mark)

Set 6   ...., ..., ...   (1 mark)

3 Use your calculator to work out the values of the following. Give your answers to 1 decimal place.

a) $5.2 + 3 + \dfrac{4 \times \sqrt{3.1^2 + 4.3^2}}{4} =$ ....   (1 mark)

b) $\dfrac{1}{4} \times 5.2 \times 3.1 + \dfrac{(3.1^2 + 7.2^2)}{2} =$ ....   (1 mark)

c) $\dfrac{2}{5} \times \dfrac{\sqrt{3.1^2 - 1.1^2}}{4} + 12^2 =$ ....   (1 mark)

Score   / 11

Total score   / 32

How well did you do?   ✗ 1–6 **Try again**   7–12 **Getting there**   13–22 **Good work**   23–32 **Excellent!** ✓

For more help on this topic see KS3 Maths 3–6 Success Guide pages 18–19.

Rounding

A

Choose just one answer, a, b, c or d.

1 **572 rounded to the nearest ten is:** (1 mark)

a) 580 ☐   b) 570 ☐   c) 575 ☐   d) 52 ☐

2 **Round 15 786 to the nearest hundred.** (1 mark)

a) 15 790 ☐   b) 15 700 ☐

c) 15 800 ☐   d) 15 780 ☐

3 **627 rounded to the nearest hundred is:** (1 mark)

a) 630 ☐   b) 610 ☐   c) 600 ☐   d) 700 ☐

4 **2794 rounded to the nearest thousand is:** (1 mark)

a) 2800 ☐   b) 2000 ☐

c) 2500 ☐   d) 3000 ☐

5 **Round 17.26 to one decimal place.** (1 mark)

a) 17.3 ☐   b) 17.2 ☐

c) 1.72 ☐   d) 1.73 ☐

6 **Round 14.635 to two decimal places.** (1 mark)

a) 14.63 ☐   b) 14.65 ☐

c) 146.35 ☐   d) 14.64 ☐

7 **Round 25.372 to one decimal place.** (1 mark)

a) 25.3 ☐   b) 25.37 ☐

c) 25.32 ☐   d) 25.4 ☐

8 **Round 279.69 to one decimal place.** (1 mark)

a) 279.7 ☐   b) 279.65 ☐

c) 279.6 ☐   d) 279.9 ☐   Score   / 8

B

Answer all parts of all questions.

1 **Round each of the following numbers to the nearest whole number.**

a) 5.7 ....   b) 6.32 ....   c) 5.45 ....   (3 marks)

2 **Round each of the following to the nearest ten.**

a) 62 ....   b) 247 ....   c) 355 ....   (3 marks)

3 **Round each of the following to the nearest hundred.**

a) 2527 ....   b) 5946 ....   c) 3755 ....   (3 marks)

4 **Read each statement and decide whether it is true or false.**

a) 2.73 rounded to 1 decimal place is 2.7. .... (1 mark)

b) 6275 rounded to the nearest ten is 6280. .... (1 mark)

c) 12.738 rounded to 2 decimal places is 12.73. .... (1 mark)

d) 25.6219 rounded to 1 decimal place is 25.2. .... (1 mark)

5 **Round each of these values to two decimal places.**

a) 16.427 ....   b) 28.391 ....   c) 37.2706 ....

d) 427.3159 ....   e) 27.275 ....   (5 marks)

6 Fill in the gaps in the table. (2 marks)

Number	to the nearest 10	to the nearest 100	to the nearest 1000
5217	....	....	....
630 573	....	....	....

Score   / 20

C

These are SATs-style questions. Answer all parts of the questions.

1 Here are some number cards:

| 5 | 9 | 1 | 3 |

Each card can be used to make a number, like this:

| 9 | 1 | 3 | 5 |

Use the four number cards to make numbers that are as close as possible to the numbers written below. For example:

4000 | 3 | 9 | 5 | 1 |

You must not use the same card more than once in each answer.

10 000 .... 5500 .... 1400 .... (3 marks)

2 The table below shows the numbers of members in three sports clubs.

Sports club	Number of members	Number of members to the nearest 100	Number of members to the nearest 10
Raceville	427	400	....
Squashton	365	....	....
Swimby	482	....	480

Complete the table to show the numbers of members to the nearest 10 and the nearest 100. (4 marks)

3 The table below shows some numbers. Round each of the numbers to the given number of decimal places and complete the table.

Number	3 decimal places	2 decimal places	1 decimal place
2.7364	....	....	....
4.2756	....	....	....
0.23865	....	....	....

(6 marks)

Score   / 13

Total score   / 41

How well did you do?   ✗ 1–10 **Try again**   11–20 **Getting there**   21–31 **Good work**   32–41 **Excellent!** ✓

Estimates & checking calculations

A

Choose just one answer, a, b, c or d.

1 Estimate the answer to this calculation:
27 × 41. (1 mark)

a) 1107 ☐   b) 1200 ☐
c) 820 ☐   d) 1300 ☐

2 Estimate the answer to this calculation:
1810 ÷ 31. (1 mark)

a) 58.4 ☐ b) 68 ☐ c) 45 ☐ d) 60 ☐

3 A bottle of water costs 51p.
Estimate the cost of 305 bottles. (1 mark)

a) £150 ☐   b) £130 ☐
c) £165 ☐   d) £156 ☐

4 Jonathan wins £12 102 on the lottery. He shares his money equally between himself and 4 other friends. Approximately how much does each receive? (1 mark)

a) £1500 ☐   b) £2900 ☐
c) £2400 ☐   d) £3000 ☐

5 Estimate the answer to this calculation:

$$\sqrt{\frac{61.1}{14.9}}$$ (1 mark)

a) 2 ☐   b) 4.1 ☐   c) 2.1 ☐   d) 4 ☐

Score   / 5   4

B

Answer all parts of all questions.

1 For each of these calculations, round the numbers to 'easy' numbers and work out an approximate answer.

a) 279 × 31 .... (1 mark)

b) 36.8 × 42.8 .... (1 mark)

c) 630 ÷ 9.9 .... (1 mark)

2 For each of the calculations below, circle the correct estimate.

	A	B	C
a) 47 × 21	400	1000	10 000
b) 298 ÷ 22	15	150	1.5
c) 1.285 × 3.9	8.5	14	4
d) 2795 ÷ 19.1	150	195	102

(4 marks)   4

3 Write down suitable calculations you could use to check the answers to the following questions.

a) 2472 ÷ 6 = 412 .... (1 mark)

b) 932 × 5 = 4660 .... (1 mark)

c) 460 + 52 = 512 .... (1 mark)

d) 1054 − 307 = 747 .... (1 mark)   4

4 Paint is sold in 8-litre tins. Gill needs 42 litres of paint. How many tins must she buy?

.... (1 mark)

Score   / 12

C Indicates that a calculator may be used

These are SATs-style questions. Answer all parts of the questions.

1 **An athletics club is taking part in the**
C **AAA Championships in Manchester.**

715 athletes are competing in the Championships.
They are going to travel by coach.
Each coach can carry 49 people.

a) How many coaches do they need
for the journey?

Show your working. .... (1 mark)

b) Each coach costs £365 to hire.

What is the total cost of the coaches?

.... (1 mark)

c) How much does each person pay to share the cost of the coaches equally?

.... (1 mark)

2 a) Circle the best estimate for the answer to: $62.57 \div 11.94$.

       3   4   5   6   7   8   (1 mark)

b) Circle the best estimate for the answer to: 49.3×19.9.

    900   1000   1100   1200   1300   (1 mark)

c) Estimate the answer to: $\dfrac{41.4 \times 20.6}{3.1 + 4.85}$

Show your working. .... (1 mark)

d) Estimate the answer to: $\dfrac{(807 \div 40.13)^2}{4.01 + 6.1}$

Show your working. .... (1 mark)

Score   / 7

Total score   / 24

How well did you do?   ✗ 1–4 Try again   5–9 Getting there   10–17 Good work   18–24 Excellent! ✓

For more help on this topic see KS3 Maths 3–6 Success Guide pages 22–23.

Ratio

A

Answer all parts of all questions.

1 **Read each of the following statements and write down if they are true or false.**

a) The ratio 20 : 10 is the same as the ratio 2 : 1. .... (1 mark)

b) The ratio 25 : 35 is the same as the ratio 4 : 5. .... (1 mark)

c) The ratio 21 : 27 is the same as the ratio 7 : 9. .... (1 mark)   3

2 **Write down each of the following ratios in the form 1 : *n*.**

a) 20 : 30 ....   b) 3 : 5 ....   c) 6 : 2 ....   (3 marks)   3

3 **The cards below have some ratios written on them:**

| 4 : 6 | 2 : 9 | 12 : 15 | 20 : 40 | 20 : 30 | 250 : 600 | 200 : 300 |

Which of the cards have the ratios equivalent to 2 : 3?... (2 marks)   2

4 **Divide each amount in the ratio given.**

a) £20 in the ratio 2 : 3. ....

b) £600 in the ratio 5 : 7. .... (2 marks)   ?

5 **A photograph of length 27cm is to be enlarged in the ratio 3 : 7.**
What is the length of the enlarged photograph? .... (1 mark)   1

6 **A recipe needs the following ingredients for 4 people. Complete the recipe for 6 people.**

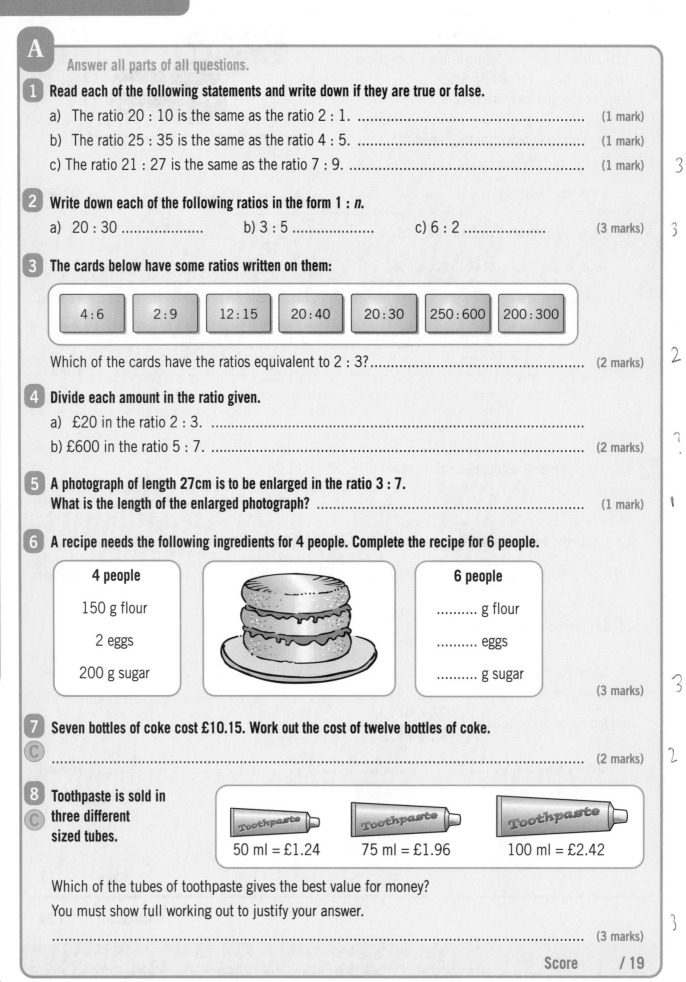

4 people		**6 people**
150 g flour		.... g flour
2 eggs		.... eggs
200 g sugar		.... g sugar

(3 marks)   3

7 **Seven bottles of coke cost £10.15. Work out the cost of twelve bottles of coke.**

Ⓒ

.... (2 marks)   2

8 **Toothpaste is sold in three different sized tubes.**

Ⓒ

50 ml = £1.24   75 ml = £1.96   100 ml = £2.42

Which of the tubes of toothpaste gives the best value for money?

You must show full working out to justify your answer.

.... (3 marks)   3

Score / 19

Ⓒ *Indicates that a calculator may be used*

These are SATs-style questions. Answer all parts of the questions.

1 One morning Ahmed carried out a survey of the cars in a car park. He saw 10 red, 20 blue, 35 black and 50 silver cars.

a) Complete the line below to show the ratios:

   i) 10 : 20 : .... : ....   (1 mark)

   ii) Now simplify the ratios. 2 : .... : .... : ....   (1 mark)

b) On another morning he carried out the survey again. He surveyed the same number of cars. The ratio of the cars this time was:

     1 : 5 : 12 : 5

Complete the table which shows the number of cars of each colour that were in the car park that morning.

Colour	Number
Red	....
Blue	....
Black	....
Silver	....

(4 marks)   4

2 A tin holds 200 g of baked beans.

C The label on the tin shows this information:

Nutritional Information		200 g tin	
Energy	150 kcal	Carbohydrate	27.3 g
Protein	9.4 g	Fat	0.4 g

a) How many grams of carbohydrate would a 450 g tin of baked beans provide?

Show your working.. (2 marks)   2

b) On a different brand of baked beans, different information is shown:

Nutritional Information		250 g tin	
Energy	165 kcal	Carbohydrate	29.0 g
Protein	10.8 g	Fat	0.62 g

A girl eats the same amount of baked beans from both tins.
Which tin provides her with more protein?

Show your working.. (2 marks)   2

Score   / 10

Total score   / 29

How well did you do?   ✗ 1–5 Try again   6–12 Getting there   13–22 Good work   23–29 Excellent!   ✓

For more help on this topic see KS3 Maths 3–6 Success Guide pages 24–25.

27

Algebra 1

A

Answer all parts of all questions.

1 Simplify the following expressions.

a) $a \times a \times a$ ....

b) $2 \times a \times 3 \times b$ ....

c) $a \times 3 \times a \times 4$ ....

d) $6 \times b^2 \times c \times b \times 2$ .... (4 marks)

2 Here are some cards with expressions.
Match the expressions with the statements.

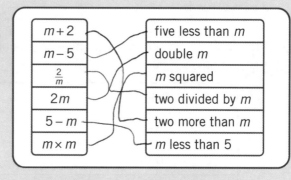

(6 marks)

3 Decide whether these expressions, which have been simplified, are true or false.

a) $5a + 2a = 7a$ ....

b) $6a + 2b - b = 6a - b$ ....

c) $3a - 5b + 2b = 3a + 3b$ ....

d) $2a + 3a - 5a + 6b - b = 5b$ ....

(4 marks)

4 For an algebra pyramid, the next layer is formed by adding the two boxes in the row below.
Complete this algebra pyramid. Write each expression as simply as possible.

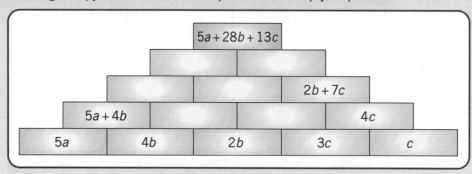

(3 marks)

5 The diagrams show some patterns made up with pink and white tiles.

Using p for the pattern number and t for the total number of tiles,
complete this formula connecting p and t.

$t =$ .... $\times p +$ ....

(2 marks)

Score   / 19

B

These are SATs-style questions. Answer all parts of the questions.

1 **Carlos has *t* counters.**

   a) Write down the following information as an expression in terms of *t*.

   (i)   Philip has five more counters than Carlos. .... (1 mark)

   (ii) Tammy has half the number of counters that Carlos has. .... (1 mark)

   (iii) Richard has three times the number of counters that Carlos has. .... (1 mark)

   (iv) Anthony has seven fewer counters than Carlos. .... (1 mark)

   b) Write down the simplest expression for the total number of counters that all five
   children have.

   .... (2 marks)

2 **These patterns are made with matchsticks:**

| pattern 1 needs | pattern 2 needs | pattern 3 needs | pattern 4 needs |
| 6 matches | 11 matches | 16 matches | 21 matches |

A rule to find how many matches are needed is: $m = 5p + 1$

m stands for the number of matches

p stands for the pattern number

   a) Use the rule to find the number of matches that would be needed in pattern
   number 10.

   Show your working.. (2 marks)

   b) If 151 matches are used for another pattern, what would its pattern number be?

   Show your working.. (2 marks)

   A different pattern is then
   made with the matches.

| pattern 1 needs | pattern 2 needs | pattern 3 needs |
| 5 matches | 9 matches | 13 matches |

   If *p* stands for the pattern number and *m* stands for the number of matches,
   write down a rule that connects *p* and *m*.

   .... (2 marks)

Score **/ 12**

Total score **/ 31**

ALGEBRA 1   Algebra

Algebra 2

A

Choose just one answer, a, b, c or d.

1 If $V = mr$ and $m = 10$ and $r = 6$, what is the value of V? (1 mark)

a) 106 ☐   b) 610 ☐   c) 60 ☐   d) 16 ☐

2 If $a = \dfrac{b}{c}$ and $b = 12$ and $c = 4$, what is the value of a? (1 mark)

a) 12 ☐   b) 4 ☐   c) 6 ☐   d) 3 ☐

3 When multiplied out, the expression $2(3x + 1)$ becomes: (1 mark)

a) $3x + 2$ ☐   b) $6x + 1$ ☐
c) $6x - 2$ ☐   d) $6x + 2$ ☐

4 When multiplied out and simplified, the expression $3(5x - 4)$ becomes: (1 mark)

a) $15x$ ☐   b) $15x - 12$ ☐
c) $5x - 12$ ☐   d) $15x - 4$ ☐

5 Factorise fully the expression $16x + 8$. (1 mark)

a) $2(8x + 4)$ ☐   b) $8(2x + 1)$ ☐
c) $8(2x)$ ☐   d) $4(4x + 2)$ ☐

6 Factorise fully the expression $20x - 10$. (1 mark)

a) $10(2x - 1)$ ☐   b) $5(4x - 2)$ ☐
c) $10(1 + 2x)$ ☐   d) $2(10x - 5)$ ☐

Score   / 6

6

B

Answer all parts of all questions.

1 If $V = IR$:

a) Calculate V when $I = 24$ and $R = 2.5$ .... (1 mark)

b) Calculate V when $I = 2.7$ and $R = 10$ .... (1 mark)

c) Calculate R when $V = 65$ and $I = 5.2$ .... (1 mark)

2

2 If $a = \dfrac{b^2 + 2c}{4}$

a) Calculate a if $b = 2$ and $c = 6$ .... (1 mark)

b) Calculate a if $b = 3$ and $c = 5.5$ .... (1 mark)

2

3 For each statement, decide whether it is true or false.

a) $3(x + 2) = 3x + 2$ ....   b) $5(2x - 1) = 10x - 5$ ....

c) $-(a + 2b) = -a - 2b$ ....   d) $2x(x + 2) = 4x^2 + 4x$ .... (4 marks)

3

4 Some expressions are written on cards. Place a card in each space provided to make the statements correct.

$\boxed{3n - 3}$ $\boxed{8(n + 2)}$ $\boxed{n^2 + 2}$ $\boxed{3n - 9}$ $\boxed{n^2 + 2n}$ $\boxed{5(n + 3)}$

a) $3(n - 3) = $ ....   b) $5n + 15 = $ ....

c) $n(n + 2) = $ ....   d) $8n + 16 = $ .... (4 marks)

4

5 Expand and simplify the following expressions.

a) $3(a + 2) = $ ....   b) $4(n - 3) = $ ....

c) $-2(a - 2) = $ ....   d) $-3(a + 1) = $ .... (4 marks)

4

Score   / 17

Ⓒ *Indicates that a calculator may be used*

These are SATs-style questions. Answer all parts of the questions.

1 Here are some algebra cards:

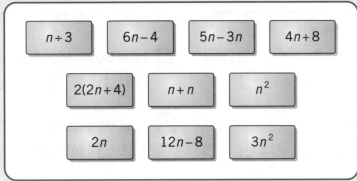

$n \div 3$ $6n - 4$ $5n - 3n$ $4n + 8$

$2(2n + 4)$ $n + n$ n^2

$2n$ $12n - 8$ $3n^2$

a) One of the cards will always give the same answer as $\dfrac{n}{3}$. Which card is it?

.... (1 mark)

b) One of the cards will always give the same answer as $n \times n$.

Which card is it? .... (1 mark)

c) Two of the cards will always give the same answer as $4(n + 2)$.

Which cards are they? .... (2 marks)

d) Write a new card which will always give the same answer as $5(n - 2)$.

.... (2 marks)

2 Nilam uses this formula to calculate the perimeter (*P*) of a shape:

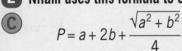

$$P = a + 2b + \frac{\sqrt{a^2 + b^2}}{4}$$

Work out the perimeter of the shape if $a = 3$ and $b = 4.2$.

Show your working. .... (2 marks)

3 a) Two of the expressions below are equivalent.
Circle them.

$3(y + 4)$ $2(4y + 3)$ $4(2y + 4)$

$3(y + 2)$ $2(4y + 8)$ $2(4y + 5)$ (1 mark)

b) Factorise the expression.

$6y + 12$ .... (1 mark)

c) Find the value of *n* if $y = 10$.

$n = 4y - 3$ .... (1 mark)

Score   / 11

Total score   / 34

How well did you do? ✗ 1–8 **Try again** 9–14 **Getting there** 15–23 **Good work** 24–34 **Excellent!** ✓

For more help on this topic see KS3 Maths 3–6 Success Guide pages 30–31.

31

ALGEBRA 2   Algebra

Equations 1

A

Choose just one answer, a, b, c or d.

1 Solve the equation $n - 3 = 7$. (1 mark)

a) 12 ☐   b) 2 ☐   c) 4 ☐   d) 10 ☐

2 Solve the equation $3n - 1 = 11$. (1 mark)

a) 12 ☐   b) 36 ☐   c) 6 ☐   d) 4 ☐

3 Solve the equation $5n + 4 = 19$. (1 mark)

a) 20 ☐   b) 3 ☐   c) 10 ☐   d) 5 ☐

4 Solve the equation $3(x + 2) = 12$. (1 mark)

a) 8 ☐   b) 6 ☐   c) 2 ☐   d) 4 ☐

5 Solve the equation $2(3 - 2y) = 3y - 8$. (1 mark)

a) 10 ☐   b) 5 ☐   c) 2 ☐   d) 6 ☐

Score   / 5

5

B

Answer all parts of all questions.

1 Solve the following equations.

a) $2n = 12$ ....

b) $\frac{n}{3} = 4$ ....

c) $n + 3 = 10$ ....

d) $n - 9 = 12$ ....

e) $n - 3 = 4$ ....

f) $5n = 25$ ....

g) $\frac{n}{6} = 1$ ....

h) $2n - 1 = 9$ ....

i) $3n + 2 = 14$ ....

j) $\frac{n}{5} + 1 = 6$ ....

k) $5n + 3 = 18$ ....

l) $7n - 1 = 13$ ....

m) $\frac{n}{3} - 4 = 2$ ....

(13 marks)

13

2 Solve the following equations.

a) $5n + 1 = 3n + 7$ ....

b) $12n - 4 = 8n + 12$ ....

c) $10n + 3 = 7n + 5$ ....

d) $15n - 1 = 3n + 11$ ....

(4 marks)

3

3 Solve the following equations.

a) $5(3x - 1) = 20$ ....

b) $7(2x + 3) = 28$ ....

c) $4(n + 5) = 3(2n + 10)$ ....

d) $2(n - 5) = 4(n + 2)$ ....

(4 marks)

3

4 Solve the following equations.

a) $5n + 6 = 3(n + 1)$ ....

b) $2n - 3 + n = 2(n + 1)$ ....

(2 marks)

1

5 The angles in a triangle add up to 180°. Form an equation in n and solve it for each of the shapes. (6 marks)

a)
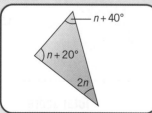

b)
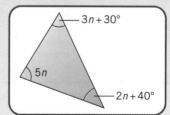

c)
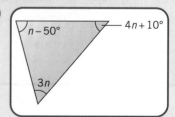

$n =$ ....

$n =$ ....

$n =$ ....

Score   / 29

2

C

These are SATs-style questions. Answer all parts of the questions.

1 In these walls, each brick is made by adding the values on the bricks beneath it.

a) i) Write an expression for the top brick in this wall. Write your expression as simply as possible.

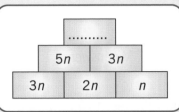

(1 mark)

ii) If the value of the top brick is 32, work out the value of n.

$n =$ .... (1 mark)

b) i) Fill in the missing expressions on this wall.

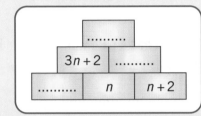

(3 marks)

ii) If the value of the top brick is 24, work out the value of n.

$n =$ .... (1 mark)

2 Solve these equations to find the values of v, w and x.

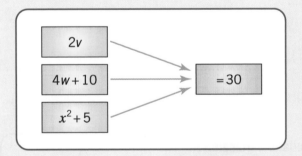

$v =$ .... $w =$ .... $x =$ ....   (3 marks)

Score   / 9

Total score   / 43

For more help on this topic see KS3 Maths 3–6 Success Guide pages 32–33.

Equations 2

A

Answer all parts of all questions.

1 Solve the following problems.

a) I multiply my number by 4 and add 3. My answer is 11.

What was my number? .... (1 mark)

b) I add 4 to my number and multiply the result by 2. My answer is 14.

What was my number? .... (1 mark)

c) I square my number and add 3. My answer is 7.

What was my number? .... (1 mark)

d) I subtract 3 from my number and then divide by 7. My answer is 3.

What was my number? .... (1 mark)

2 John and Rameen were playing a game. John had a card with $5n + 4$ and Rameen had a card with $3n - 6$. For what value of n are the cards equal?

.... (2 marks)

3 Jeremy says, 'Multiplying my number by 3 and adding 4 gives the same answer as subtracting my number from 20.'

What is Jeremy's number? .... (2 marks)

4 Using a trial and improvement method, solve the following equations, giving your answers to 1 decimal place.

a) $a^2 - 28 = 0$.. (1 mark)

b) $a^2 - 104 = 0$.. (1 mark)

c) $a^3 - a = 15$.. (1 mark)

5 The diagram shows an equilateral triangle.

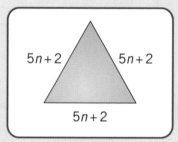

If the total length of the sides add up to 51 cm, work out the value of n.

.... (2 marks)

Score   / 13

C *Indicates that a calculator may be used*

B

These are SATs-style questions. Answer all parts of the questions.

1 The lengths of a triangle are given in the diagram.
The perimeter of the triangle is 32 cm.

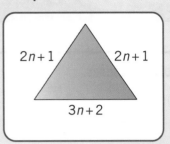

a) Write down an expression for the perimeter of the triangle, as simply as possible.

.... (1 mark)

b) Given that the perimeter of the triangle is 32 cm, form an equation and solve it to find the length of each side.

Equations: ....

Lengths: ...., ..., ...   (4 marks)

2
C
Annabelle makes a rectangle with an area of 24.5 cm².
The sides of Annabelle's rectangle are
n cm and $(10 - n)$ cm.

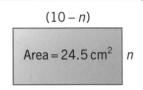

$(10 - n)$

Area = 24.5 cm² n

She wants to find a value of n, to one decimal place,
which gives her an area as close as possible to 24.5 cm².
Using the table below, find the value of n, to one decimal place.

n	$10 - n$	Area
2	8	16

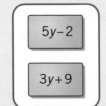

4.3

$n =$ .... (1 d.p.)   (3 marks)

3 Two cards have different expressions:

$5y - 2$

and $3y + 9$

For what value of y are the values of the expressions
on the two cards equal? $y =$ .... (2 marks)

Score   / 10

Total score   / 23

How well did you do?   ✗ 1–4 **Try again**   5–9 **Getting there**   10–16 **Good work**   17–23 **Excellent!**   ✓

For more help on this topic see KS3 Maths 3–6 Success Guide pages 34–35.

Number patterns & sequences

A

Answer all parts of all questions.

1 a) Using this function machine, if the input value is 7, what is the output?

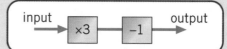

.... (1 mark)

b) Using the function machine, if the output value is 10, what is the input value?

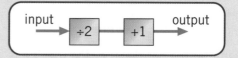

.... (1 mark)

2 **For each of the sequences below, write down the next two terms.**

a) 2, 4, 6, 8, ..., ...   b) 4, 7, 10, 13, ..., ...

c) 1, 4, 9, 16, ..., ...   d) 12, 6, 3, 1.5, ..., ...   (4 marks)

3 **Look at the numbers in the cloud.**

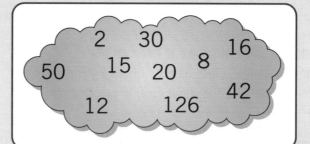

Write down the numbers from the cloud that are:

a) divisible by 2 .... (1 mark)

b) divisible by 3 .... (1 mark)

c) divisible by 5 .... (1 mark)

d) divisible by both 2 and 5 .... (1 mark)

4 **Grace has written a sequence of numbers: 4, 7, 10, 13**

a) Write down the next three terms in Grace's sequence........................ (1 mark)

b) What is the 10th term of this sequence?... (1 mark)

c) What is the nth term of this sequence?... (1 mark)

5 **Look at this sequence of numbers: 6, 8, 10, 12**

a) What is the next number in the sequence?.. (1 mark)

b) Write down the nth term of this sequence....................................... (1 mark)

c) What is the 12th term of this sequence?... (1 mark)

6 **For each of these sequences, decide whether the nth term given is true or false.**

a) 2, 4, 6, 8, 10 nth term: $n + 2$ .... (1 mark)

b) 1, 4, 7, 10, 13 nth term: $3n - 2$ .... (1 mark)

c) 1, 4, 9, 16, 25 nth term: n^2 .... (1 mark)

Score   / 19

B

These are SATs-style questions. Answer all parts of the questions.

1 a) Here is a number chain: $3 \rightarrow 5 \rightarrow 7 \rightarrow 9 \rightarrow$

The rule is: **add on 2 each time**

A different number chain is: $1 \rightarrow 4 \rightarrow 7 \rightarrow 10 \rightarrow$

What could the rule be? .... (1 mark)

b) Some number chains start like this: $1 \rightarrow 2 \rightarrow$

Show two different ways to continue the number chain. For each chain write down the next three numbers.

First chain $1 \rightarrow 2 \rightarrow$ .... $\rightarrow$ .... $\rightarrow$ ....

The rule is .... (2 marks)

Second chain $1 \rightarrow 2 \rightarrow$ .... $\rightarrow$ .... $\rightarrow$ ....

The rule is .... (2 marks)

2 The diagram shows some stick patterns.

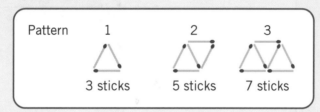

Pattern   1   2   3

3 sticks   5 sticks   7 sticks

a) Complete the table below.

Pattern number	1	2	3	4	5	6
Number of sticks	3	5	7			

(3 marks)

b) How many sticks are needed for pattern number 20? .... (1 mark)

c) Write down a rule which would help you to work out the number of sticks needed for pattern number n.

.... (1 mark)

3 The nth term of a sequence is $3n + 1$. What is the 8th term in the sequence?

.... (1 mark)

Score   / 11

Total score   / 30

For more help on this topic see KS3 Maths 3–6 Success Guide pages 36–37.

Coordinates & graphs

A

Answer all parts of all questions.

1 a) Complete the tables of values for the following lines:

i) $y = 2x$

x	-2	-1	0	1	2	3
y						

ii) $y = 3x - 2$

x	-1	0	1	2	3
y					

(2 marks)

b) Draw the graphs:

$y = 2x$ and $y = 3x - 2$
on the grid opposite

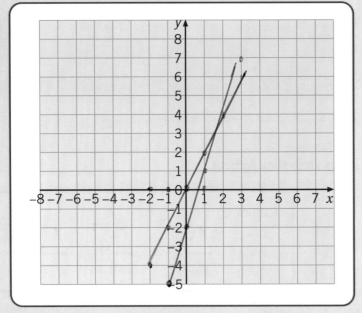

(2 marks)

2 **Find the gradient of each of these lines:**

a) Gradient of AB ....

b) Gradient of CD ....

c) Gradient of EF ....

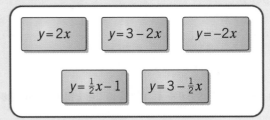

(3 marks)

3 **The following** **have some**

equations of lines. Match each of the cards with the correct information.

$y = 2x$ $y = 3 - 2x$ $y = -2x$

$y = \frac{1}{2}x - 1$ $y = 3 - \frac{1}{2}x$

a) The gradient is -2 and the intercept is at $(0, 3)$ .... (1 mark)

b) The gradient is $\frac{1}{2}$ and the intercept is at $(0, -1)$ .... (1 mark)

c) The gradient is 2 and the intercept is at $(0, 0)$ .... (1 mark)

d) The gradient is $-\frac{1}{2}$ and the intercept is at $(0, 3)$ .... (1 mark)

e) The gradient is -2 and the intercept is at $(0, 0)$ .... (1 mark)

Score   / 12

B

These are SATs-style questions. Answer all parts of the questions.

1 The diagram shows the graph of the line $y = 3x$.

a) Write down the coordinates of the following points:

A = (................, ...)

B = (................, ...)

C = (................, ...)   (3 marks)

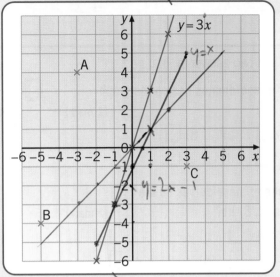

b) Draw the graph of the straight line $y = x$ on the axes.

Label the line $y = x$.   (1 mark)

c) Write the equation of another straight line which goes through the point (0, 0).

$y =$ .... (1 mark)

d) The straight line with the equation $y = 2x - 1$ goes through the point (3, 5).

i) Work out two more coordinates that lie on the line $y = 2x - 1$.

(................, ...)   (................, ...)   (2 marks)

ii) On the diagram, draw the graph of the straight line $y = 2x - 1$.

Label your line $y = 2x - 1$.   (2 marks)

e) Write the equation of a straight line that goes through the point (0, –4) and is parallel to the straight line $y = 3x$.

$y =$ .... (1 mark)

2 Here are five different equations, labelled A to E.

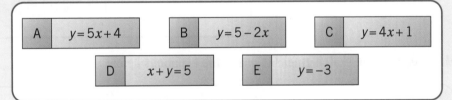

Think about the graphs of these equations.

a) Which graph goes through the point (0, 1)? .... (1 mark)

b) Which graph is parallel to the x-axis? .... (1 mark)

c) Which graph is parallel to $y = 5x - 2$? .... (1 mark)

d) Which two graphs meet at point (0, 5)? .... and .... (2 marks)

Score   / 15

Total score   / 27

How well did you do?   ✗ 1–5 Try again   6–12 Getting there   13–20 Good work   21–27 Excellent!   ✓

For more help on this topic see KS3 Maths 3–6 Success Guide pages 38–39.

More graphs

A

Choose just one answer, a, b, c or d.

1 Which pair of coordinates lies on the graph $y = x^2$? *(1 mark)*

a) (−1, −4) ☐   b) (2, 8) ☐

c) (4, 16) ☐   d) (1, 9) ☐

2 On which one of these curves do the coordinates (2, 6) lie? *(1 mark)*

a) $y = 2x^2 + 6x$ ☐   b) $y = 3x^2 − 1$ ☐

c) $y = x^2 − 4$ ☐   d) $y = x^2 + 2$ ☐

3 On which one of these curves do the coordinates (3, 26) lie? *(1 mark)*

a) $y = x^3 − 1$ ☐   b) $y = x^3$ ☐

c) $y = x^2 − 4x$ ☐   d) $y = 2x^2 + 1$ ☐

Score   / 3

3

B

Answer all parts of all questions.

1 Write down the equations of the lines drawn on the grid opposite. The first has been done for you.

(4 marks)

a) Line A: $x = 4$
....

b) Line B: ....

c) Line C: ....

d) Line D: ....

e) Line E: ....

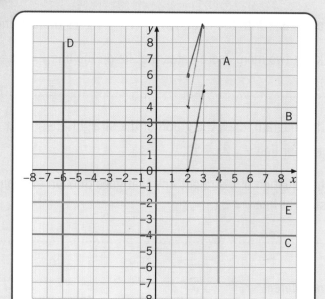

2 Match each of the sketch graphs to one of the equations below. *(5 marks)*

| $y = x^2$ | $y = x^2 + 1$ | $y = x^3$ | $y = 2x^2 − 3$ | $y = x^2 − 6$ |

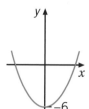 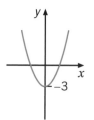 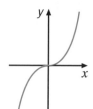 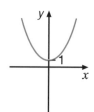

a) ....   b) ....   c) ....   d) ....   e) ....

5

Score   / 9

C

These are SATs-style questions. Answer all parts of the questions.

1 The table below shows the values of x and y for the equation $y = x^2 - 4$.

a) Complete the table.

x	−2	−1	0	1	2	3
y				−3	0	5

(2 marks)

b) On the grid below, draw the graph of $y = x^2 - 4$.
Make sure you label the graph.

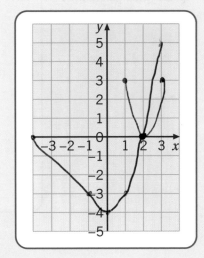

(2 marks)

c) On the same grid, sketch the graph of $y = x^2 + 2$. (1 mark)

d) Write down the equation of the line of symmetry for both of these graphs.

.... (1 mark)

2 Here are six different equations, labelled A to F:

A	$y = x^2 - 4$	B	$y = x^2$	C	$y = 3x$
D	$y = 4 - x^2$	E	$x + y = 12$	F	$y = x^3$

Think about the graphs of these equations.

a) Which three graphs go through the point (0, 0)?

.................., ... and .... (3 marks)

b) Which graph goes through the point (3, 27)? .... (1 mark)

c) Which graphs are symmetrical about the y-axis? .... (1 mark)

d) Which graph goes through the point (1, 3)? .... (1 mark)

Score   / 12

Total score   / 24

How well did you do?   ✗ 1–5 Try again   6–13 Getting there   14–19 Good work   20–24 Excellent!   ✓

For more help on this topic see KS3 Maths 3–6 Success Guide pages 40–41.

Using linear graphs

A   Answer all parts of all questions.

1 This conversion graph converts British pounds (£) into euros (€) and vice versa.

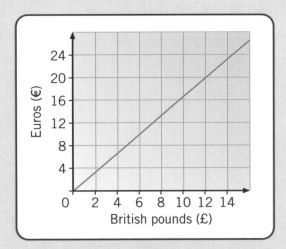

Use the graph to convert:

a) £10 into euros .... (1 mark)

b) €16 into pounds .... (1 mark)

2 Amy has a mobile phone. Her mobile has this tariff:

Monthly charge £10
Calls cost 10p per minute

a) Complete the table, which shows Amy's costs:

Number of minutes	0	10	20	30	40	50	60
Cost (£)	10			13			

(2 marks)

b) Draw a graph of the costs on the axis provided.

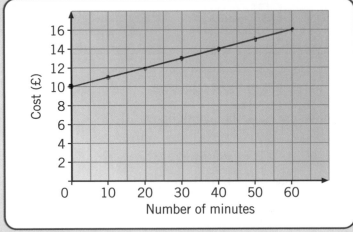

(1 mark)

c) How much would 35 minutes of calls cost?

.... (1 mark)

d) If Amy pays £25 one month, for how many minutes did she use the phone?

.... (1 mark)

e) Explain why Amy's bill cannot be less than £10.

.... (1 mark)

Score   / 8

B

These are SATs-style questions. Answer all parts of the questions.

1 Here are four containers. Water is poured at a constant rate into three of the containers. The graphs show the depth of the water as the containers fill up.

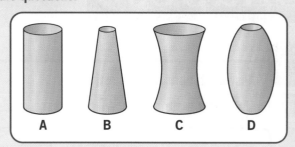

A   B   C   D

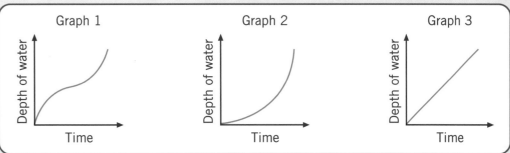

Graph 1   Graph 2   Graph 3

Depth of water / Time   Depth of water / Time   Depth of water / Time

Fill in the gaps below to show which container matches each graph.

Graph 1 matches container ....   Graph 2 matches container ....

Graph 3 matches container ....   (3 marks)   2

2 The simplified graph shows the journey of a taxi travelling from London to St Albans.

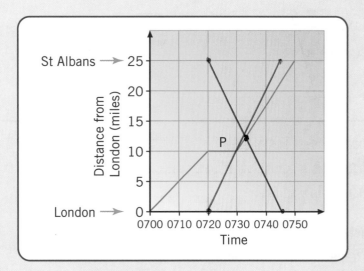

a) What is the taxi's average speed from London to St Albans? .... mph   (1 mark) ✓

b) Explain what has happened at P.

....   (1 mark) ✓

c) A different taxi travels from St Albans to London. It sets off at 0720 and drives at a constant speed directly to London, arriving at 0745.

On the graph, show the taxi's journey from St Albans to London.   (2 marks) 2

d) At approximately what time do the two taxis pass each other?

....   (1 mark) ✓

Score   / 8

Total score   / 16

How well did you do?   ✗ 1–2 Try again   3–6 Getting there   7–11 Good work   12–16 Excellent!   ✓

For more help on this topic see KS3 Maths 3–6 Success Guide pages 42–43.

Shapes

A

Answer all parts of all questions.

1 The following are triangles. Which of these words best describe them?

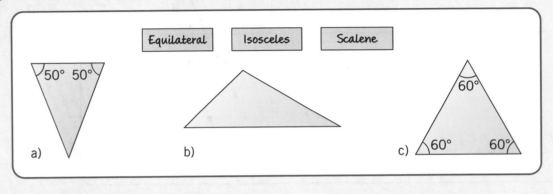

a) ....   b) ....   c) .... (3 marks)

2 The following lettered shapes are quadrilaterals. Decide whether each of the statements is true or false.

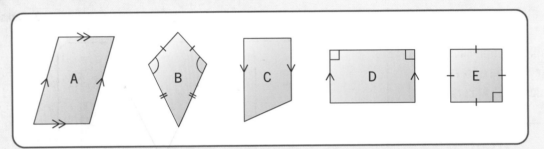

a) Shape A is a parallelogram. ....   b) Shape B is a kite. ....

c) Shape C is a parallelogram. ....   d) Shape D is a rectangle. ....

e) Shape E is a square. ....

(5 marks)

3 Complete the missing words in these statements.

a) A trapezium has one pair of .... sides.

b) A parallelogram has rotational symmetry of order ....

c) A square has .... lines of symmetry.

d) The perimeter of a circle is known as the ....

e) The radius and tangent to a point make an angle of .... (5 marks)

4 Draw a regular hexagon. (1 mark)

a) How many lines of symmetry does it have?... (1 mark)

b) What is its order of rotational symmetry? .... (1 mark)

Score   / 16

Letts KS3 Success

Workbook Answer Booklet

Mathematics SATs

Levels 3-6

Answers

Pages 6–7 Numbers 1
A
1. b
2. c
3. b
4. d
5. c
6. b

B
1. a) Four hundred and three
   b) Three thousand, six hundred and twenty-seven
2. a) 645
   b) 2 000 304
3. a) Tens
   b) Units
   c) Hundred thousands
4. a) 7431
   b) 7134 (or any combination that does *not* have 7 first)
   c) 1374
5. a) 64, 421, 506, 1462, 1731, 3702
   b) 2, 27, 275, 846, 1362, 2701

C
1. a) Hannah 406
      Matthew 95
      Robert 169
   b) 78, 95, 169, 406
2. a) 76 321
   b) 12 376
3. Any number from between 2001 to 2199

Pages 8–9 Numbers 2
A
1. a
2. d
3. c
4. d
5. a
6. b

B
1. a) 1, 4, 6, 12
   b) 13, 17
   c) 1, 4, 49
   d) 6, 12
2. a) False
   b) True
   c) False
   d) True
3. 1, 4, 9, 16, 25, 36
4. 24
5. 2
6. $2 \times 2 \times 3 \times 5$
7. False
8. 1, 2, 3, 4, 6, 8, 12, 24
9. a) $4^3 = 4 \times 4 \times 4$
   b) $2^5 = 2 \times 2 \times 2 \times 2 \times 2$

C
1. a)
   b)
   c)

Number of rows	Number of counters in each row
1 row	12 counters in each row
2 rows	6 counters in each row
3 rows	4 counters in each row
4 rows	3 counters in each row
6 rows	2 counters in each row
12 rows	1 counter in each row

   d) 5 is not a factor of 12.
2. Penelope's number is 16.
   Tom's number is 2.

Pages 10–11 Positive & negative numbers
A
1. a) $-3 < 6$
   b) $-4 > -10$
   c) $7 > -6$
   d) $0 > -3$
2. a) -3 and -7
   b) 0 and -7
   c) 5 and -3
3. a) 12
   b) 8
   c) 12
   d) -3
   e) 3
   f) -4
4. a) 21
   b) -5
   c) -2
   d) -16
5. $-22°C$
6.

		4		
	7		-3	
	4	3	-6	
7	-3	6	-12

7. a) $-12 \div -3 = 4$
   b) $-7 - (-3) = -4$
   c) $9 \div -3 = -3$
   d) $12 + (-5) = 7$

B
1. a) Arrow points to 32°C
   b) Arrow points to –7°C
   c) –2°C
   d) 12°C
   e) 15°C, 9°C, 0°C, –3°C, –6°C, –12°C
2. a) –1
   b) –5
   c) 5
   d) –5
   e) 3
   f) –5

Pages 12–13 Working with numbers
A
1.

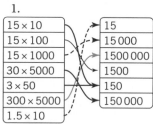

2. a) 30
   b) 50
   c) 13
3.

6	1	8
7	5	3
2	9	4

4. a) 769
   b) 341
   c) 10 872
   d) 137
5. a) 11 718
   b) 529 620
   c) 45
   d) 83
6. £26.64
7. 42
8. £8190

B
1. a) 178
   b) 1285
   c) 4
   d) 8712
2. a) 270 pencils
   b) £24.50
   c) £10.50
   d) 12 boxes
3. $170 - 110$
   $31 + 29$
   $\frac{1}{4}$ of 240
   $1200 \div 20$
4. a) £249.75
   b) (i) 33 shrubs
      (ii) 220 grams
5.

   a)

		4		0

   b)

4	2	7	0	0	0

Pages 14–15 Fractions
A
1. a) $\frac{4}{8} = \frac{1}{2}$
   b) $\frac{3}{5}$
   c) $\frac{2}{5}$
2. a) $\frac{2}{9} = \frac{6}{27}$
   b) $\frac{3}{5} = \frac{15}{25}$
   c) $\frac{27}{99} = \frac{9}{33} = \frac{3}{11}$
   d) $\frac{10}{17} = \frac{30}{51}$

3. a) $\frac{2}{8} = \frac{1}{4}$
   b) $\frac{4}{20} = \frac{1}{5}$
   c) $\frac{6}{12} = \frac{1}{2}$
   d) $\frac{25}{35} = \frac{5}{7}$
4. a) $\frac{7}{2} = 3\frac{1}{2}$
   b) $\frac{4}{3} = 1\frac{1}{3}$
   c) $\frac{5}{3} = 1\frac{2}{3}$
   d) $\frac{10}{4} = 2\frac{1}{2}$
5. a) $\frac{31}{35}$
   b) $\frac{3}{26}$
6. a) $\frac{2}{9}, \frac{1}{3}, \frac{1}{2}, \frac{4}{7}, \frac{4}{5}$
   b) $\frac{2}{7}, \frac{1}{3}, \frac{3}{5}, \frac{9}{13}$
7. a) $\frac{8}{63}$
   b) 4
8. a) True
   b) False
   c) False
   d) True
9. 70
10. 210

B
1. a) 4 cakes
   b) $\frac{12}{16} = \frac{3}{4}$
   c) 16 cakes
2. $\frac{4}{9}$ of 18
   20% of 40
   $\frac{2}{3}$ of 12
   One-half of 16
3. a) £30
   b) £600
   c) $\frac{31}{35}$
   d) $\frac{8}{35}$
4. a) $\frac{5}{16}$
   b) £26.25

Pages 16–17 Decimals
A
1. a
2. d
3. a
4. d

B
1. a) Six thousandths
   b) Six tenths
   c) Six units
   d) Six hundredths
2. a) True
   b) True
   c) False
   d) True
3. 2.71, 3.62, 3.69, 3.691, 4.38, 4.385, 4.39
4.

		34.5		
	14.2		20.3	
	6.3	7.9	12.4	
2.7	3.6	4.3	8.1

5. a) Tom
   b) 0.085
6. £69.48
7. a) 10
   b) 100
   c) 10
   d) 1000
   e) 1000
   f) 1000

C
1. a) 6.4
   b) 16.6
   c) 281.25
   d) 15.6
2. a) $2.7 \times 3.05 = 8.235$
   b) $3.05 \times 1000 = 3050$
   c) $4.6 \div 100 = 0.046$

Pages 18–19 Percentages
A
1. a) 27%
   b) 38%
2. £99 000
3. £110.50
4.

10% of 60	→	32
25% of 200	→	45
40% of 80	→	6
15% of 120	→	18
30% of 150	→	50

5. £22.56
6. a) Maths   80%
      English 54%
      German   38%
      Science 81%
   b) German
7. a) 39%
   b) 80%

B
1. a) 6 grams
   b) £65
   c) £150
   d) 279 litres
2. a) 41.7%
   b) 18.6%
   c) 12.9%
3. a) (i) £1.30
      (ii) £9.75
   b) £143.28

Pages 20–21 Equivalents & using a calculator
A
1. a) 60%, 0.6
   b) 12.5%, 0.125
2. a) 0.25
   b) $\frac{3}{10}$
   c) 12.5%
3. 25%, 30%, $\frac{3}{8}$, $\frac{2}{5}$, 0.41, 72%, 0.9
4. Supers = £380
   Electricals = £408
   Ramones = £440.63
   Supers is the cheapest.
5. They are both right since $30\% = \frac{3}{10}$.
6. a) 11
   b) 36
   c) 15

7. a) 0.7317
   b) 0.2097
   c) 73.0974
      (all to 4 d.p.)

B
1. $\frac{2}{5}$, 0.4, 40%
   $\frac{1}{2}$, 0.5, 50%
   $\frac{1}{8}$, 0.125, 12.5%
   $\frac{15}{20}$, 0.75, 75%
2. 90%, 0.9, $\frac{9}{10}$
   33.$\dot{3}$%, 0.$\dot{3}$, $\frac{1}{3}$
   37.5%, 0.375, $\frac{3}{8}$
   5%, 0.05, $\frac{1}{20}$
3. a) 13.5 (1 d.p.)
   b) 34.8 (1 d.p.)
   c) 144.3 (1 d.p.)

Pages 22–23 Rounding
A
1. b
2. c
3. c
4. d
5. a
6. d
7. d
8. a

B
1. a) 6
   b) 6
   c) 5
2. a) 60
   b) 250
   c) 360
3. a) 2500
   b) 5900
   c) 3800
4. a) True
   b) True
   c) False
   d) False
5. a) 16.43
   b) 28.39
   c) 37.27
   d) 427.32
   e) 27.28
6.

Number	to nearest 10	to nearest 100	to nearest 1000
5217	5220	5200	5000
630 573	630 570	630 600	631 000

C
1. 10 000: 9531
   5500:   5391
   1400:   1395
2.

Sports club	Number of members	Number of members to nearest	
		100	10
Raceville	427	400	430
Squashton	365	400	370
Swimby	482	500	480

3.

Number	3 decimal places	2 decimal places	1 decimal place
2.7364	2.736	2.74	2.7
4.2756	4.276	4.28	4.3
0.23865	0.239	0.24	0.2

Pages 24–25 Estimates & checking calculations
A
1. b
2. d
3. a
4. c
5. a

B
1. a) 9000
   b) 1600
   c) 60
2. a) B
   b) A
   c) C
   d) A
3. a) $412 \times 6 = 2472$
   b) $4660 \div 5 = 932$
   c) $512 - 52 = 460$
   d) $747 + 307 = 1054$
4. 6 tins of paint

C
1. a) 15 coaches
   b) £5475
   c) £7.66
2. a) 5
   b) 1000
   c) 100
   d) 40

Pages 26–27 Ratio
A
1. a) True
   b) False
   c) True
2. a) 1 : 1.5
   b) 1 : 1.$\dot{6}$.
   c) 1 : 0.$\dot{3}$.
3. 4 : 6, 20 : 30 and 200 : 300
4. a) 8 : 12
   b) 250 : 350
5. 63cm
6. 225g flour
   3 eggs
   300g sugar
7. £17.40
8. The 100ml tube of toothpaste

B
1. a) (i) 10 : 20 : 35 : 50
      (ii) 2 : 4 : 7 : 10
   b)

Colour	Number
Red	5
Blue	25
Black	60
Silver	25

2. a) 61.43g (2 d.p.)
   b) 200g tin provides 0.047 gram of protein per gram of beans. 250g tin provides 0.0432 gram of protein per gram of beans, so the 200g tin provides more protein.

Pages 28–29 Algebra 1
A
1. a) a^3
   b) $6ab$
   c) $12a^2$
   d) $12b^3c$
2.

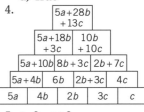

$m+2$		five less than m
$m-5$		double m
$\frac{2}{m}$		m squared
$2m$		two divided by m
$5-m$		two more than m
$m \times m$		m less than 5

3. a) True
   b) False
   c) False
   d) True
4.

		$5a+28b$ $+13c$		
	$5a+18b$ $+3c$		$10b$ $+10c$	
	$5a+10b$	$8b+3c$	$2b+7c$	
$5a+4b$	$6b$		$2b+3c$	$4c$
$5a$	$4b$	$2b$	$3c$	c

5. $t = 2 \times p + 3$

B
1. a) (i) $t+5$
      (ii) $\dfrac{t}{2}$
      (iii) $3t$
      (iv) $t-7$
   b) $\dfrac{11t}{2} - 2$ or $5.5t - 2$
2. a) $5 \times 10 + 1 = 51$ matches
   b) pattern number 30
   c) $m = 4p + 1$

Pages 30–31 Algebra 2
A
1. c
2. d
3. d
4. b
5. b
6. a

B
1. a) 60
   b) 27
   c) 12.5
2. a) 4
   b) 5
3. a) False
   b) True
   c) True
   d) False
4. a) $3(n-3) = 3n-9$
   b) $5n + 15 = 5(n+3)$
   c) $n(n+2) = n^2 + 2n$
   d) $8n + 16 = 8(n+2)$
5. a) $3a + 6$
   b) $4n - 12$
   c) $-2a + 4$
   d) $-3a - 3$

C
1. a) $n \div 3$
   b) n^2
   c) $4n + 8$ and $2(2n + 4)$
   d) $5n - 10$

2. a) $P = 3 + (2 \times 4.2) + \frac{\sqrt{3^2 + 4.2^2}}{4}$
   $P = 12.69$
3. a) $4(2y + 4)$ and $2(4y + 8)$
   b) $6(y + 2)$
   c) $n = 37$

Pages 32–33 Equations 1

A

1. d
2. d
3. b
4. c
5. c

B

1. a) $n = 6$
   b) $n = 12$
   c) $n = 7$
   d) $n = 21$
   e) $n = 7$
   f) $n = 5$
   g) $n = 6$
   h) $n = 5$
   i) $n = 4$
   j) $n = 25$
   k) $n = 3$
   l) $n = 2$
   m) $n = 18$
2. a) $n = 3$
   b) $n = 4$
   c) $n = \frac{2}{3}$
   d) $n = 1$
3. a) $x = \frac{5}{3}$
   b) $x = \frac{1}{2}$
   c) $n = -5$
   d) $n = -9$
4. a) $n = -\frac{3}{2}$
   b) $n = 5$
5. a) $n = 30°$
   b) $n = 11°$
   c) $n = 27.5°$

C

1. a) (i) $8n$
   (ii) $n = 4$
   b) (i)

	$5n + 4$	
$3n + 2$		$2n + 2$
$2n + 2$	n	$n + 2$

   (ii) $n = 4$
2. $v = 15$
   $w = 5$
   $x = \pm 5$

Pages 34–35 Equations 2

A

1. a) 2
   b) 3
   c) 2 or –2
   d) 24
2. $n = -5$
3. 4
4. a) $a = 5.3$
   b) $a = 10.2$
   c) $a = 2.6$
5. $n = 3$

B

1. a) $7n + 4$
   b) $7n + 4 = 32$
   $7n = 32 - 4$
   $7n = 28$
   $n = 4$
   Lengths: 9 cm, 9 cm, 14 cm
2. $n = 4.3$
3. $5y - 2 = 3y + 9$
   $y = 5.5$

Pages 36–37 Number patterns & sequences

A

1. a) 20
   b) 18
2. a) 10, 12
   b) 16, 19
   c) 25, 36
   d) 0.75, 0.375
3. a) 2, 8, 12, 16, 20, 30, 42, 50, 126
   b) 12, 15, 30, 42, 126
   c) 15, 20, 30, 50
   d) 20, 30, 50
4. a) 16, 19, 22
   b) 31
   c) $3n + 1$
5. a) 14
   b) $2n + 4$
   c) 28
6. a) False
   b) True
   c) True

B

1. a) Add on 3 each time
   b) Lots of possible answers; justification needed
2. a)

Pattern number	1	2	3	4	5	6
Number of sticks	3	5	7	9	11	13

   c) 41
   d) $2n + 1$, multiply pattern number by 2 and add 1
3. 25

Pages 38–39 Coordinates & graphs

A

1. i) $y = 2x$

x	–2	–1	0	1	2	3
y	–4	–2	0	2	4	6

   ii) $y = 3x - 2$

x	–1	0	1	2	3
y	–5	–2	1	4	7

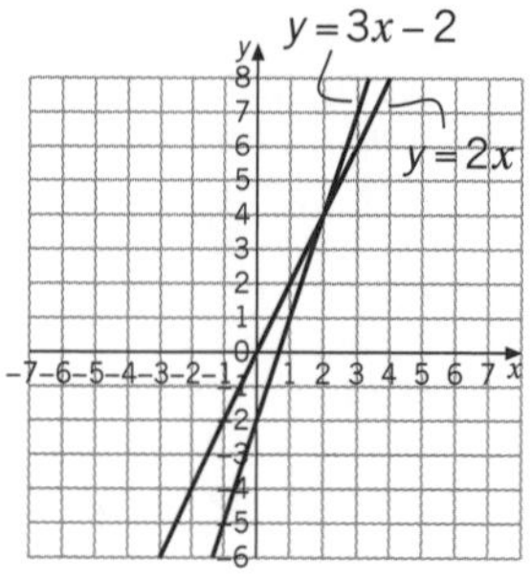

2. Gradient of AB = 1 unit
   Gradient of CD = –3 units
   Gradient of EF = $\frac{1}{2}$ unit
3. a) $y = 3 - 2x$
   b) $y = \frac{1}{2}x - 1$
   c) $y = 2x$
   d) $y = 3 - \frac{1}{2}x$
   e) $y = -2x$

B

1. a) A = (–3, 4)
   B = (–5, –4)
   C = (3, –1)
   b)

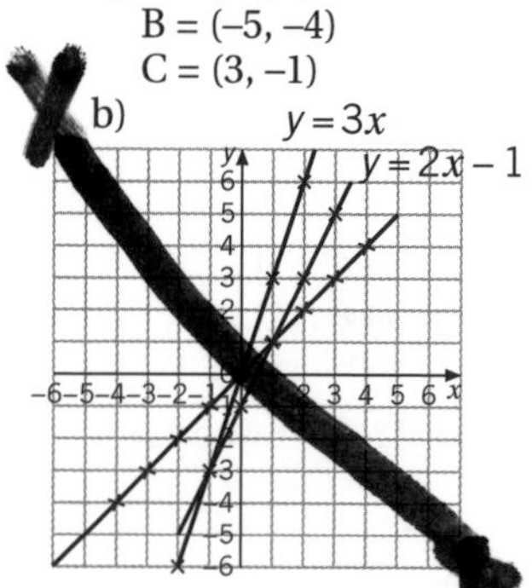

   c) $y = 4x$, $y = 2x$, $y = -3x$ etc. any graph of the form $y = nx$
   d) (i) (2, 3) (0, –1) (or any two points with $y = 2x - 1$)
   (ii) See graph above
   e) $y = 3x - 4$
2. a) C: $y = 4x + 1$
   b) E: $y = -3$
   c) A: $y = 5x + 4$
   d) B: $y = 5 - 2x$ and D: $x + y = 5$

Pages 40–41 More graphs

A

1. c
2. d
3. a

B

1. b) Line B: $y = 3$
   c) Line C: $y = -4$
   d) Line D: $x = -6$
   e) Line E: $y = -2$
2. a) $y = x^2$
   b) $y = 2x^2 - 3$
   c) $y = x^2 - 6$
   d) $y = x^3$
   e) $y = x^2 + 1$

C

1. a)

x	–2	–1	0	1	2	3
y	0	–3	–4	–3	0	5

   b) c)

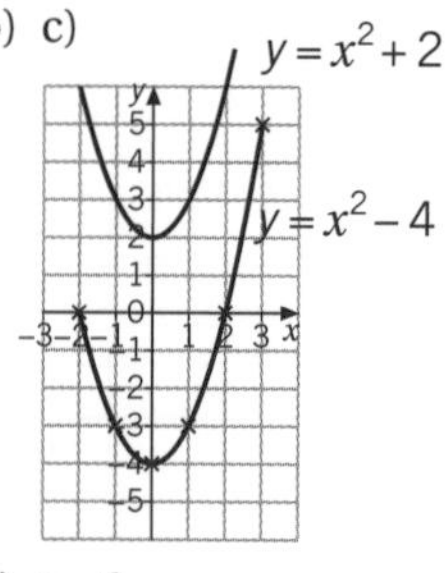

   d) $x = 0$

2. a) B y
   F y
   b) F y
   c) A y
   D y
   d) D $y = 4 - x^2$

Pages 42–43 Using linear graphs

A

1. a) €16.67 (approx. €16.50)
   b) £9.60 (approx. £9.50)
2.

Number of minutes	0	10	20	30	40	50	60
Cost (£)	10	11	12	13	14	15	16

   b)

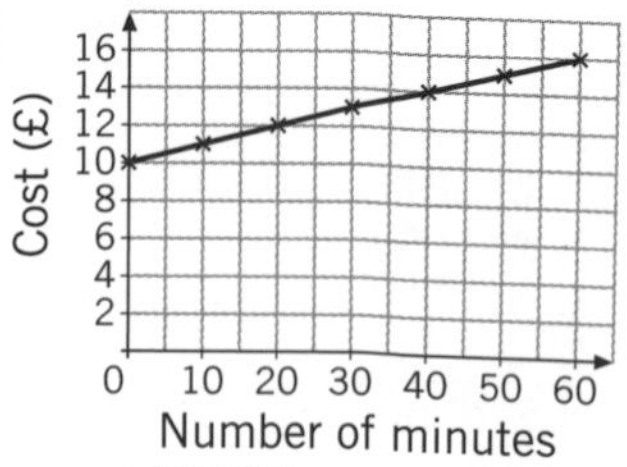

   c) £13.50
   d) 150 minutes
   e) Even if Amy does not use her phone, she has to pay the £10 standing charge. So her bill will never be less than £10.

B

1. Graph 1 matches container D.
   Graph 2 matches container B.
   Graph 3 matches container A.
2. a) 30 mph
   b) Taxi has stopped.
   c)

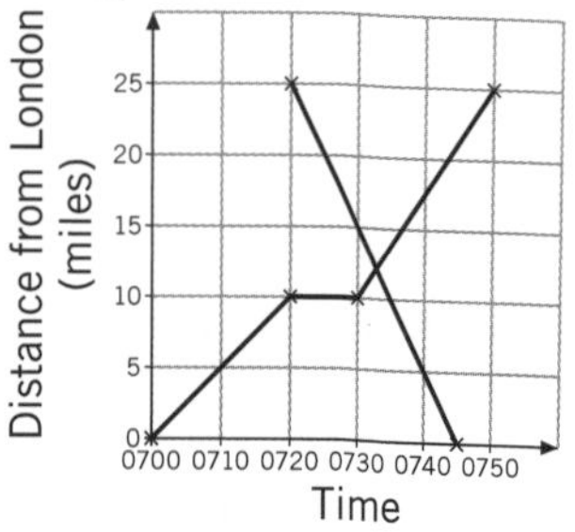

   d) 0733

Pages 44–45 Shapes

A

1. a) isosceles
   b) scalene
   c) equilateral
2. a) True
   b) True
   c) False
   d) True
   e) True
3. a) parallel
   b) 2
   c) 4
   d) circumference
   e) 90°

4.

a) 6
b) 6

B
1. a) Trapezium and quadrilateral
   b) equilateral, 3, 60
2. a) Pentagon
   b) Quadrilateral
   c) Octagon
   d) Heptagon
3.

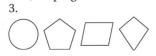

Pages 46–47 Solids
A
1. c
2. c
3. a
4. d
5. c

B
1. a) Cuboid
   b) Cylinder
   c) Triangular prism
2. Nets a, b, e
3. a)
   b)

C
1. a)

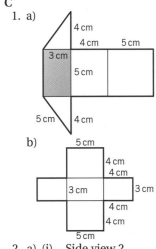

   4 cm
   4 cm   5 cm
   3 cm
   5 cm
   5 cm   4 cm

   b)
   5 cm
   4 cm
   4 cm
   3 cm   3 cm
   4 cm
   4 cm
   5 cm

2. a) (i) Side view 2
      (ii) Side view 1
      (iii) Side view 4
      (iv) Side view 3
   b)

Pages 48–49 Symmetry
A
1. c
2. a
3. c
4. d
5. c

B
1.

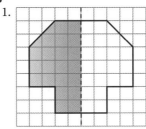

2. a) Order 2
   b) Order 4
   c) Order 4
3.

a)   b)   c)

C
1.

	Number of lines of symmetry				
		0	1	2	3	4
Order of rotational symmetry	1		F			
	2	E		A		
	3				B,D	
	4					C

2. a) All shapes should be identical on both sides.
   b)

3. a) 2 planes of symmetry
   b)
   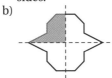

Pages 50–51 Constructions & logo
A
1. Forward 6
   Turn right 120°
   Forward 6
   Turn right 120°
   Forward 6
2. Accurate diagrams to be drawn. Lengths accepted which are ± 2 mm.
3. Accurate diagrams to be drawn, lengths to be accurate to ± 2 mm, angles to ± 2°.
4. Perpendicular bisector to be drawn cutting AB at 3.5cm.
5. Line bisects angle at 30°.

B
1. a) Forward 12
   Turn right 90°
   Forward 12
   Turn right 90°
   Forward 12
   Turn right 90°
   Forward 12

   b) Forward 5
      Turn right 60°
      Forward 3
      Turn right 120°
      Forward 5
      Turn right 60°
      Forward 3
2. Accurate drawing, lengths accurate to ±2 mm

Pages 52–53 Angles & tessellations
A
1. a) Acute: 7°, 27°, 41°
   b) Obtuse: 98°, 104°, 117°
   c) Reflex: 275°, 325°
2. a) 60°
   b) 80°
   c) 163°
   d) 138°
   e) 65°
   f) 102°
3. a) $a = 130°$
      $b = 50°$
      $c = 50°$
   b) $a = 60°$
      $b = 60°$
      $c = 120°$

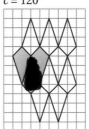

B
1. a) 180°
   b) 90°
2. a) (i) $a = 80°$
      (ii) $b = 20°$
   b) $a = 65°$
      $b = 95°$
      $c = 150°$
3. (i) $a = 60°$
      $b = 120°$
   (ii) Three regular hexagons tessellate at a point, since $3 × 120° = 360°$. Shapes will only tessellate when the angles add up to 360°.

Pages 54–55 Bearings & scale drawings
A
1. c
2. b
3. b
4. d

B
1. a) True
   b) False
   c) False
2. a) (i) 072°
      (ii) 252°
   b) (i) 310°
      (ii) 130°

c) (i) 230°
   (ii) 050°
d) (i) 150°
   (ii) 330°
3. 10 km

C
1. a) Accurate diagram to be drawn, lengths to be accurate to ±2 mm, angles, to ±2°.
   b) 9.4 cm
2.

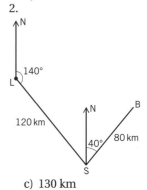

   c) 130 km

Pages 56–57 Transformations
A
1.

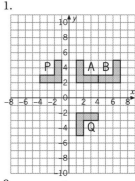

2

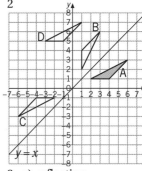

3. a) reflection
   b) translation
   c) rotation
   d) reflection

B
1.

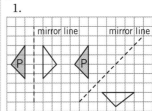

2.

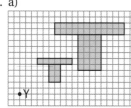

3. a)

b) 3 cm and 15 cm

Pages 58–59 Measures & measurement 1

A
1. d
2. b
3. b
4. c
5. b

B
1. a) 1 metre
   b) 5 metres
2. a) 7000 m
   b) 0.6 m
   c) 0.5 m
   d) 2.5 kg
   e) 6000 kg
   f) 2600 ml
   g) 0.53 kg
   h) 5.8 l
3. Approx. 1.1 gallons
4. 12.5 miles
5. a) Approx. 4 metres
   b) Approx. 384 km
   c) Approx. 5 ml

C
1. a) 11.4 cm
   b) 7.2 cm
2. Reece has more sweets because 3 ounces is approximately 85g.
3. 12.5 cm
4. a) 6000 ml
   b) Since 1 litre is approximately 1.75 pints, then a 6-litre jug must hold more than 6 pints, not less as Lucy says.

Pages 60–61 Measures & measurement 2

A
1. c
2. d
3. a
4. c
5. d
6. b

B
1.

12-hour clock	4.47 pm	1.34 pm	7.26 pm	2.36 pm	2.17 am	9.40 pm
24-hour clock	1647	1334	1926	1436	0217	2140

2. a) 60
   b) 52
   c) 604 800
3. a) Thursday
   b) Sunday
4. a) 17 minutes
   b) 0106
   c) 0744

C
1. a) 1 hr 35 minutes
   b) 19.50
2. a) 20 minutes
   b) 50 minutes
   c) 27 minutes
   d) 87 minutes
3. a) 0810
   b) 0930

Pages 62–63 Area & perimeter of 2D shapes

A
1. 60 m
2. a) distance
   b) space
3. a) (i) $P = 12$ cm
      (ii) $A = 6$ cm^2
   b) (i) $P = 20.57$ cm
      (ii) $A = 25.13$ cm^2
   c) (i) $P = 25.13$ cm
      (ii) $A = 50.27$ cm^2
   d) (i) $P = 46.8$ cm
      (ii) $A = 61.09$ cm^2
4. a) 122.5 cm^2
   b) 63.6 cm

B
1. a) 4 cm
   b) 5 cm
2. 21.94 cm^2
3. a) 1256.6 cm^2
   b) 1570.8 cm^2

Pages 64–65 Volume of 3D solids

A
1. a) 12 cm^3
   b) 15 cm^3
2.

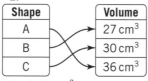

Shape	Volume
A	27 cm^3
B	30 cm^3
C	36 cm^3

3. a) 24 cm^3
   b) 52 cm^2
4. 1080 cm^3
5. 682.5 cm^3

B
1. Cuboid drawn with volume 24 cm^3 i.e.
   $1 \times 1 \times 24$ $2 \times 2 \times 6$
   $2 \times 1 \times 12$ etc.
   $3 \times 1 \times 8$
   $4 \times 1 \times 6$
2. 8.1 cm
3. 198 cm^3
4. 1920 cm^3

Pages 66–67 Collecting data

A
1. b
2. c
3. d

B
1. a) Secondary data
   b) Continuous data
   c) Primary data
   d) Discrete data
2.

Eye colour	Tally	Frequency

3.

4	2	8	7	2	4	
5	4	3	0	6	4	9
6	1	7	3	9		
7	3	1	1			

reordered →

4	2	2	4	7	8	
5	0	3	4	4	6	9
6	1	3	7	9		
7	1	1	3			

C
1. a)

Book type	Tally	Frequency
Crime	ⅧⅠ III	8
Horror	ⅧⅠ II	7
Fiction	ⅧⅠ ⅧⅠ I	11
Science fiction	III	3

   b) Fiction
   c) Molly was correct as only three science fiction books had been sold.
2. a) The middle three boxes overlap with each other, for example: age 15 could be placed in two boxes.
   A good answer would be:
   b) less than 1 hour
      1 up to 2 hours
      2 up to 3 hours
      3 hours and over

Pages 68–69 Representing information

A
1. a) True
   b) False
   c) True
   d) True
   e)

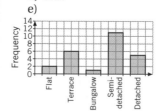

2. a) 120°
   b) 8 hours
   c) 6 hours

B
1. a)

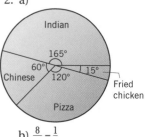

   b)

Time (t minutes)	Frequency
$0 \leqslant t < 5$	12
$5 \leqslant t < 10$	8
$10 \leqslant t < 15$	5
$15 \leqslant t < 20$	4
$20 \leqslant t < 25$	1

   c) He is correct as two-thirds of the people queue for less than 10 minutes.
2. a)

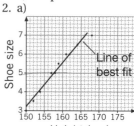

   b) $\frac{8}{24} = \frac{1}{3}$

Pages 70–71 Scatter diagrams & misleading graphs

A
1. a) Graph X
   b) Graph Z
   c) Graph Y
   d) Graph Y
   e) Graph Z
2. a)

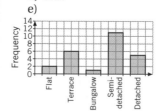

   b) Positive correlation
   c) 155.5cm

B
1. The scale does not start at zero, so the growth looks much bigger than it actually is.
2. a) Positive correlation – the longer the hours spent revising, the higher the maths score.
   b) Negative correlation – the longer the hours spent watching the television, the lower the maths score.

c) Zero or no correlation
d) Approx. 76%

Pages 72–73 Averages 1

A

1.

Data	Mean
1, 2, 3, 4, 5	6
1.4, 2.8, 3.1, 4.2, 5.6	29.8
9, 21, 30, 38, 51	3
10, 20, 30, 40, 50	3.42
2, 4, 6, 8, 10	30

(with arrows connecting data to means)

2. a) 3.2
   b) 2.5
   c) 2
   d) 6
3. 32 cm
4. She has found the middle card but she did not put them in order of size first.

B

1. a) 8
   b) (i) 9
      (ii) 8
      (iii) 9
   c) (i) 5
      (ii) 10
2. 7, 7, 13

Pages 74–75 Averages 2

A

1. a
2. b
3. d
4. b

B

1. a) 47.64
   b) The mode is 48 and the mean is 47.64; this supports the manufacturer's claim that there are, on average, 48 matches in each box.
2. He is not correct. Although the mean height of class B is greater than the mean height of class A, the range for class B is much larger so there may be some students who are smaller than the students in class A.

C

1. a) 33
   b) 27.26
   c) 27
2. a) 1.9
   b) Mode = 2
      Median = 2
3. Company B – the mean length was the same but the range was much smaller, hence the nails were probably more consistent in length.

Pages 76–77 Probability 1

A

1. a) Impossible
   b) Evens chance
   c) Certain
   d) Likely
   e) Unlikely
2. a) $\frac{3}{13}$
   b) $\frac{6}{13}$
   c) 0
   d) $\frac{7}{13}$
3. a) $\frac{15}{28}$
   b) $\frac{13}{28}$
   c) 0
4. a) Rupinder is incorrect because the spinner is not divided equally into 3 sectors. The number 3 occupies half of the spinner.
   b) $\frac{1}{2}$
5. a) True
   b) False
   c) False

B

1. a) She is wrong because there are more yellow beads than red beads.
   The probability of choosing a red is $\frac{2}{5}$.
   b)

   c) $\frac{1}{2}$
2. a) Spinner Y because 3 occupies 2 of the spaces and not just 1 as on spinner X.
   b) Spinner X because $\frac{3}{4}$ of the spinner has even numbers.
3. 12

Pages 78–79 Probability 2

A

1. c
2. b
3. c
4. a

B

1. (ham, tea); (cheese, tea); (beef, tea); (ham, coffee); (cheese, coffee); (beef, coffee)
2. 42 races
3. 140 people
4. a)

	2	4	6	8
3	6	12	18	24
5	10	20	30	40
5	10	20	30	40
7	14	28	42	56

   b) $\frac{16}{16} = 1$
   c) $\frac{2}{16} = \frac{1}{8}$

C

1. a) K1 K2 K3 K4 K5 K6
      L1 L2 L3 L4 L5 L6
      M1 M2 M3 M4 M5 M6
      18 combinations
   b) $\frac{1}{3}$
2. 6 races
3. a) $\frac{7}{16}$
   b) $\frac{10}{16} = \frac{5}{8}$

SATs Exam Papers
Non-calculator questions

1. a) Half
   b) Less than half
   c) More than half
2. a) 543
   b) 482
   c) 450
   d) 91
3.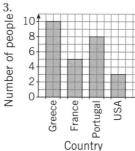
4. a) Reflex
   b) 53 degrees
5. £14.20
6. a) 67.8
   b) 678
   c) 13.56
   d) 3, 5 and 7
7.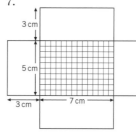
8. a)

Square spinner

Triangle spinner	2	3	4	5
1	2	3	4	5
2	4	6	8	10
5	10	15	20	25

   b) $\frac{4}{12} = \frac{1}{3}$
   c) $\frac{3}{12} = \frac{1}{4}$
   d) 2
   e) $\frac{3}{12} = \frac{1}{4}$
9. a) (i) 15
      (ii) 5
      (iii) 11
   b) $n = 8$
   c) $y = 3$
10. $a = 52°$
    $b = 76°$
    $c = 60°$
    $d = 30°$
    $e = 30°$

Calculator questions

1. a) 327
   b) 703
   c) 597
2. a) 66
   b)
   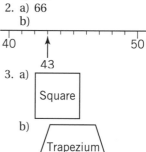
3. a)
   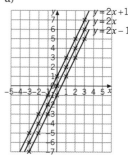
   b)
4. a) True, because each number has an equally likely chance of appearing.
   b) False, this is the expected probability but it is not certain to happen.
5. a) £2.43
   b) £10.50
   c) £52.50
6. a) (i) $2n + 2s$
      (ii) $4n + 2e + 6$
      (iii) $5b + 2c + 2e$
   b) $y = 4$
7. a) 20%
   b) $\frac{12}{30} = \frac{2}{5}$ of the pupils
   c)

	Skating	Cinema	Bowling
Number of pupils	3	15	12

   d) 1 : 5 : 4
   e) $\frac{3}{30} = \frac{1}{10}$
8. a) $4n + 5$
   b) 32 cards
9. a) The older the car becomes the lower the value, or it has negative correlation.
   b) £2250 to £3250
   c) It may have been involved in a crash, may be damaged or badly rusted etc.
   d) Between 5 and 6 years old.
10. a)

   b) See graph
   c) The 2x helps decide if they are parallel, since 2 is the gradient of each line.

d) $y = 2x - 4$ etc. (any line as long as $y = 2x$ forms part of the equation).

e) The constant, i.e. $y = 2x + 1$ (any indication of the constant).

f) $(0, -10)$

Mental Arithmetic Test

1. 40
2. 70 minutes
3. 77 pence
4. 6 faces
5. 360 degrees
6. 14
7. 6
8. 4
9. 5 : 2
10. 3500 metres
11. 180 seconds
12. 16
13. Trapezium
14. 28
15. 138
16. 13
17. 3.3
18. 30 degrees
19. $8a + 2b$
20. £11.96
21. £8
22. 7
23. £80
24. $\frac{3}{7}$
25. circle B
26. 90
27. 36 cm^2
28. 6
29. 30 km
30. 3 and 12

ACKNOWLEDGEMENTS

The author and publisher are grateful to the copyright holders for permission to use quoted materials and photographs.

Letts Educational
4 Grosvenor Place
London SW1X 7DL

School enquiries: 01539 564910
Parent & student enquiries: 01539 564913
E-mail: mail@lettsed.co.uk
Website: www.letts-educational.com

First published 2007

Text © Fiona C. Mapp 2007
Design and illustration © Letts Educational Limited 2007

British Library Cataloguing in Publication Data.
A CIP record of this book is available from the British Library.

ISBN: 9781843157632

Book concept and development: Helen Jacobs, Letts Publishing Director

Letts editorial team: Marion Davies and Alan W

Author: Fiona C. Mapp

Cover design: Angela English
Inside concept design: Starfish Design
Text design, layout and editorial:
MCS Publishing Services

B

These are SATs-style questions. Answer all parts of the questions.

1 a) Look at this shape. Two of the statements below are correct.
Tick the correct statements.

The shape is a hexagon.　　　　□

The shape is a quadrilateral.　　□

The shape is a kite.　　　　　　□

The shape is a trapezium.　　　□

The shape is a parallelogram.　□

(1 mark)

b) Look at this shape. Complete these statements about the shape.

The shape is an .... triangle. The shape has .... lines of symmetry.
Each angle is .... degrees.

(3 marks)

2 Some names of polygons have been written on cards.

| Pentagon | Hexagon | Heptagon | Quadrilateral | Octagon |

Write down the name of the polygon for each of the shapes below, choosing from the list above.

a)　　　　　　b)　　　　　　c)　　　　　　d)

a) ....　　b) ....

c) ....　　d) ....　(4 marks)

3 In the spaces provided, draw an example of each of the shapes listed.

a) Circle　　　　　　　　　　b) Pentagon

c) Parallelogram　　　　　　d) Kite　　　　　(4 marks)

a)　　　　b)　　　　c)　　　　d)

Score　　/ 12

Total score　　/ 28

How well did you do?　　✗ 1–5 **Try again**　6–12 **Getting there**　13–21 **Good work**　22–28 **Excellent!**　✓

For more help on this topic see KS3 Maths 3–6 Success Guide pages 46–47.

45

SHAPES

Shape, space & measures

Solids

A

Choose just one answer, a, b, c or d.

Questions 1–5 relate to the diagrams below.

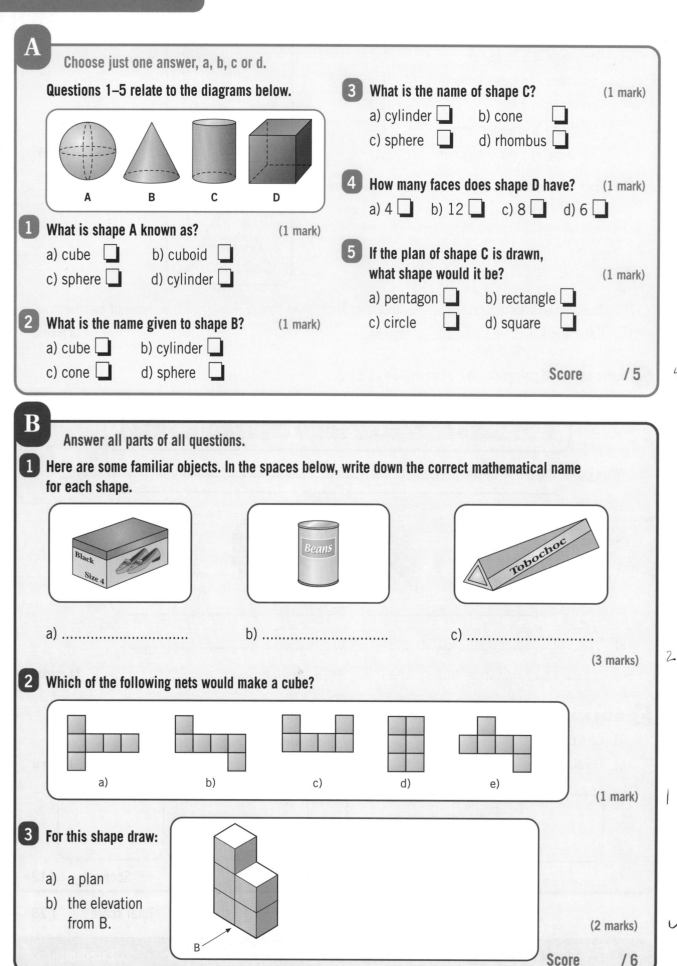

A   B   C   D

1 What is shape A known as?   (1 mark)

a) cube ☐   b) cuboid ☐

c) sphere ☐   d) cylinder ☐

2 What is the name given to shape B?   (1 mark)

a) cube ☐   b) cylinder ☐

c) cone ☐   d) sphere ☐

3 What is the name of shape C?   (1 mark)

a) cylinder ☐   b) cone ☐

c) sphere ☐   d) rhombus ☐

4 How many faces does shape D have?   (1 mark)

a) 4 ☐   b) 12 ☐   c) 8 ☐   d) 6 ☐

5 If the plan of shape C is drawn, what shape would it be?   (1 mark)

a) pentagon ☐   b) rectangle ☐

c) circle ☐   d) square ☐

Score   / 5   4

B

Answer all parts of all questions.

1 Here are some familiar objects. In the spaces below, write down the correct mathematical name for each shape.

Black
Size 4

Beans

Tobochoc

a) ....   b) ....   c) ....

(3 marks)   2

2 Which of the following nets would make a cube?

a)   b)   c)   d)   e)

(1 mark)   1

3 For this shape draw:

a)   a plan

b)   the elevation from B.

B

(2 marks)   ✓

Score   / 6

46

These are SATs-style questions. Answer all parts of the questions.

1 Jeremy is making a box to hold a small chocolate egg.
He decides to draw a sketch of the net of the box.
The base of the box is shaded.

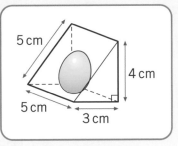

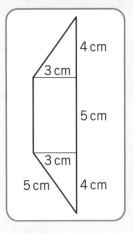

a) Complete the sketch of the net of the box. (1 mark)

b) Jacqueline is also making a box to hold a
small chocolate egg.
Her box has no lid.
Draw a net for the box.

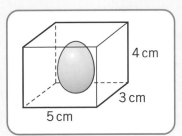

(3 marks)   3

2 Opposite is a diagram showing a model
made from 9 cubes. The cubes are either
purple or white. There are five purple
cubes and four white cubes.

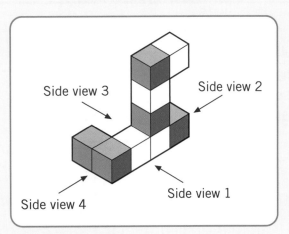

a) The drawings below show the side views of the model.
Write numbers to show which side view each drawing represents.

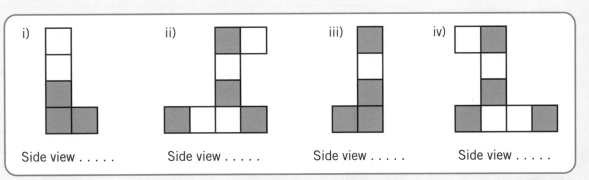

i) Side view . . . . .   ii) Side view . . . . .   iii) Side view . . . . .   iv) Side view . . . . .

(2 marks)

b) Draw the top view of the model, making sure you shade the purple cubes. (2 marks)   2

Score   / 8

Total score   / 19

How well did you do?   ✗ 1–3 Try again   4–7 Getting there   8–13 Good work   14–19 Excellent!   ✓

For more help on this topic see KS3 Maths 3–6 Success Guide pages 48–49.

Symmetry

A

Choose just one answer, a, b, c or d.

1 How many lines of symmetry does a rectangle have? *(1 mark)*

a) 6 ☐   b) 4 ☐   c) 2 ☐   d) 8 ☐

2 How many lines of symmetry does this shape have? *(1 mark)*

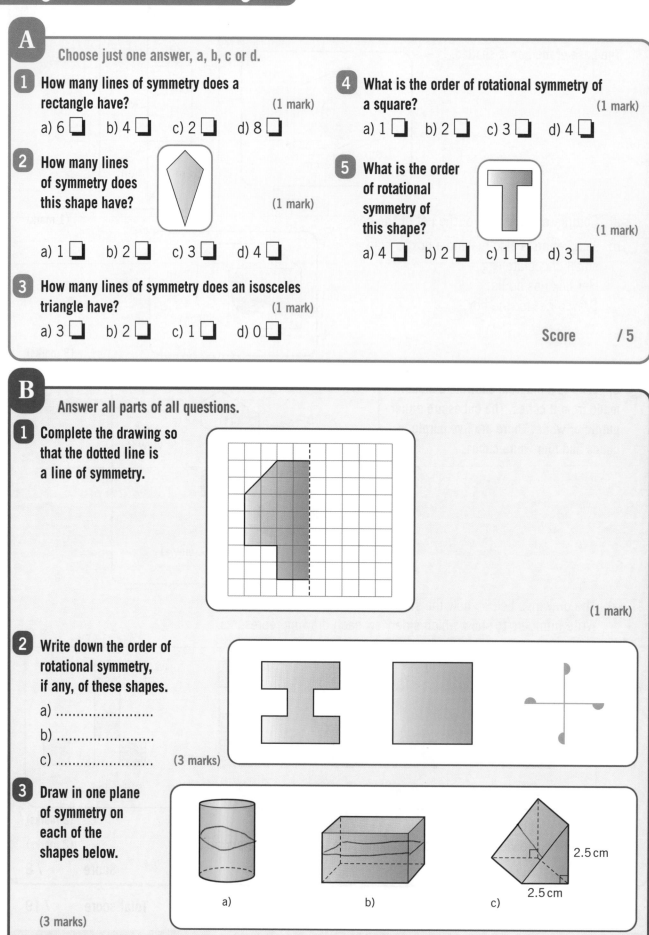

a) 1 ☐   b) 2 ☐   c) 3 ☐   d) 4 ☐

3 How many lines of symmetry does an isosceles triangle have? *(1 mark)*

a) 3 ☐   b) 2 ☐   c) 1 ☐   d) 0 ☐

4 What is the order of rotational symmetry of a square? *(1 mark)*

a) 1 ☐   b) 2 ☐   c) 3 ☐   d) 4 ☐

5 What is the order of rotational symmetry of this shape? *(1 mark)*

a) 4 ☐   b) 2 ☐   c) 1 ☐   d) 3 ☐

Score   / 5

B

Answer all parts of all questions.

1 Complete the drawing so that the dotted line is a line of symmetry.

(1 mark)

2 Write down the order of rotational symmetry, if any, of these shapes.

a) ....

b) ....

c) .... *(3 marks)*

3 Draw in one plane of symmetry on each of the shapes below.

a)   b)   c)

2.5 cm

2.5 cm

(3 marks)

Score   / 7

48

C

These are SATs-style questions. Answer all parts of the questions.

1 Here are some shapes:

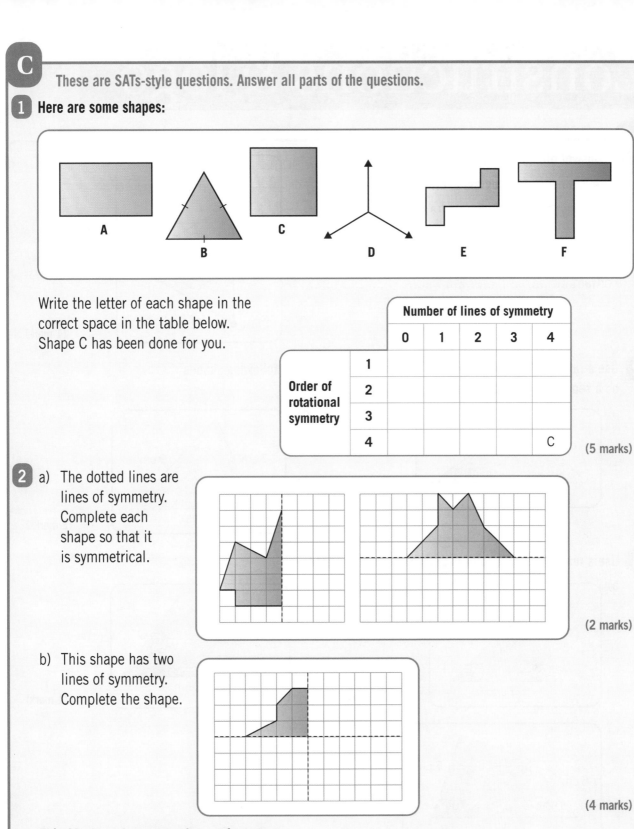

A   B   C   D   E   F

Write the letter of each shape in the
correct space in the table below.
Shape C has been done for you.

		Number of lines of symmetry				
		0	1	2	3	4
	1					
Order of rotational symmetry	2					
	3					
	4					C

(5 marks) 3

2 a) The dotted lines are
lines of symmetry.
Complete each
shape so that it
is symmetrical.

(2 marks)

b) This shape has two
lines of symmetry.
Complete the shape.

(4 marks)

This 3D shape has some planes of symmetry.

a) How many planes of symmetry
does this shape have?   ....

(1 mark)

b) Draw in one plane of symmetry
on the shape.·

(1 mark)

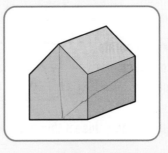

Score   / 13   6

Total score   / 25

Constructions & logo

A

Answer all parts of all questions.

1 Here is a computer program to draw a triangle:

Complete the instructions to draw this shape.

Forward 6

Turn right 120°

Forward ....

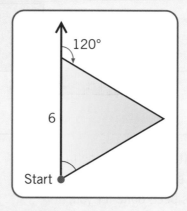

(1 mark)

2 Use a ruler and compasses to draw accurate diagrams of the following shapes on a separate piece of paper.

a)

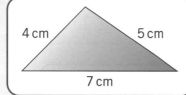

(2 marks)

b)

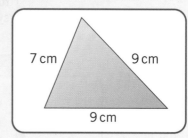

(2 marks)

3 Use a ruler and a protractor to draw the following shapes.

a)

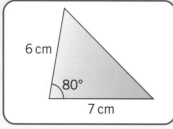

(1 mark)

b)

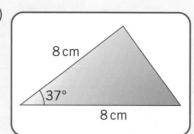

(1 mark)

c)

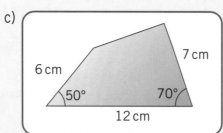

(1 mark)

4 Copy this line AB onto a separate piece of paper and construct the perpendicular bisector.

A————————————————B

(2 marks)

5 Using ruler and compasses only, bisect this angle.

(2 marks)

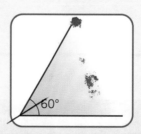

Score   / 12

50

B

These are SATs-style questions. Answer all parts of the questions.

1 **Shape A is a square.**

The instructions to draw shape A are:

Forward 4
Turn right 90°
Forward 4
Turn right 90°
Forward 4
Turn right 90°
Forward 4

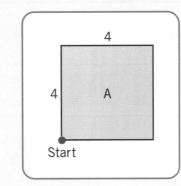

a) Write down the instructions to draw a square that has sides three times the length of those of shape A.

....

....

.... (2 marks)

b) Shape B is a parallelogram.
Complete the instructions to draw shape B.
Forward 5
Turn right 60°

....

....

....

....

....

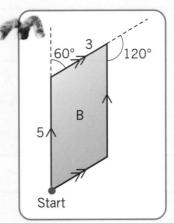

(2 marks)

2 **Joshua has made a rough sketch of this triangle.**

Using ruler and compasses, construct the triangle accurately in the space provided.

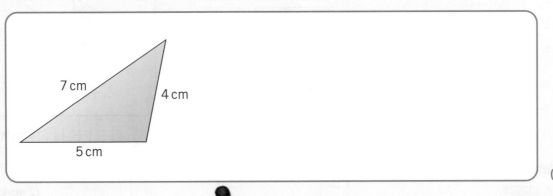

(2 marks)

Score   / 6

Total score   / 18

How well did you do?   ✗ 1–3 Try again   4–7 Getting there   8–13 Good work   14–18 Excellent!   ✓

For more help on this topic see KS3 Maths 3–6 Success Guide page 51.

Angles & tessellations

A

Answer all parts of all questions.

1 Some angles are written on cards:

| 27° | 7° | 98° | 41° | 117° | 104° | 275° | 325° |

Which of the angles are:

a) acute ....   b) obtuse ....   c) reflex ....   (3 marks)   *3*

2 Work out the size of the angle *a* in each of the diagrams.

C

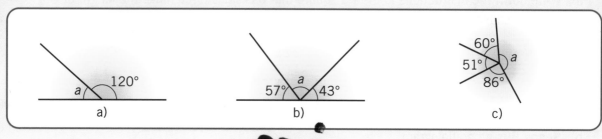

a)   b)   c)

a = ...   *a* =    *a* = ...   *3*

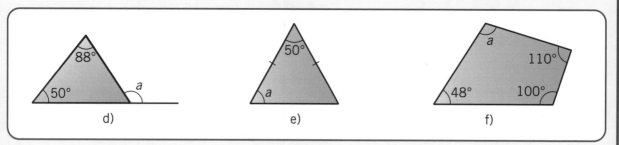

d)   e)   f)

a = ...   *a* = ...   *a* = ... (6 marks)   *3 =6*

3 Calculate the size of the angles marked with letters.

a)   *a* = ...

    b = ...

    c = ...

b)   *a* = ...

    b = ...

    c = ...

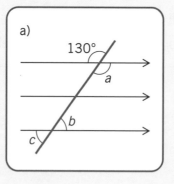

a)

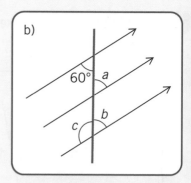

b)

(6 marks)   *6*

4 Complete this tessellation by drawing 6 more shapes.

(2 marks)

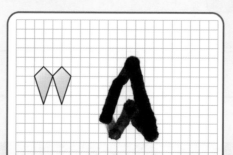

Score   / 17

C *Indicates that a calculator may be used*

B

These are SATs-style questions. Answer all parts of the questions.

1 The time on this clock is 6 o'clock.

a) What is the size of the angle between the two hands? ....° (1 mark)

b) What is the size of the angle between the two hands at 3 o'clock? ....° (1 mark)

2 a) Fiona has drawn a shape, using her computer.

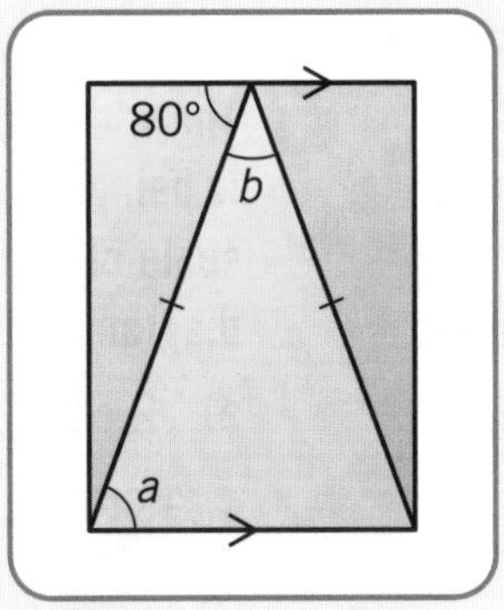

The diagram shows an isosceles triangle inside a rectangle.

i) Calculate the size of the angle marked *a*. $a =$ ....° (1 mark)

ii) Calculate the size of the angle marked *b*. $b =$ ....° (1 mark)

b) Simon has drawn this shape with his computer.

Calculate angles *a*, *b* and *c*.
Show your working.

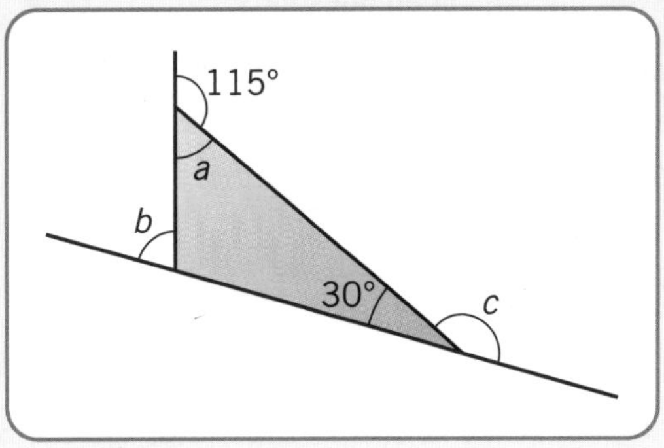

$a =$ ....

$b =$ ....

$c =$ .... (3 marks)

c) Simon draws a second shape with his computer.

It is a regular hexagon.

(i) Calculate the sizes of angles *a* and *b*.
Show your working.

$a =$ ....

$b =$ .... (2 marks)

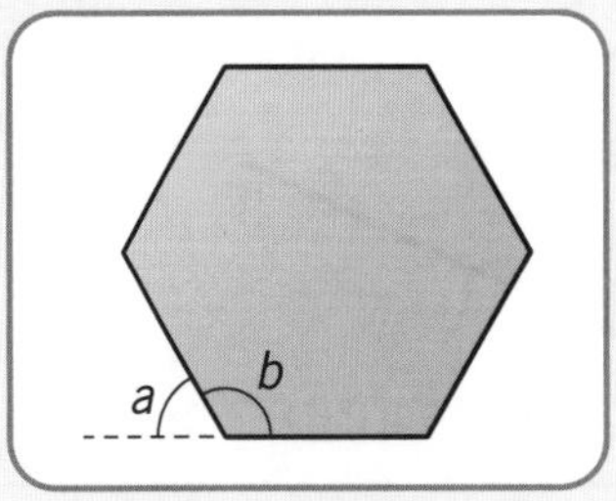

(ii) Explain why a regular hexagon will tessellate.

.... (1 mark)

Score   / 10

Total score   / 27

How well did you do? ✗ 1–6 **Try again**   7–13 **Getting there**   14–21 **Good work**   22–27 **Excellent!** ✓

For more help on this topic see KS3 Maths 3–6 Success Guide pages 52–53.

53

Bearings & scale drawings

A

Choose just one answer, a, b, c or d.

1 Audrey is facing south. If she turns through an angle of 270° clockwise, in what direction will she now be facing? *(1 mark)*

a) north ☐ b) south ☐

c) east ☐ d) west ☐

2 Colin is facing north west. If he turns through an angle of 180°, what direction will he now be facing? *(1 mark)*

a) north ☐ b) south east ☐

c) south ☐ d) west ☐

3 The bearing of A from B is 060°. What is the bearing of B from A? *(1 mark)*

a) 60° ☐ b) 240° ☐

c) 120° ☐ d) 200° ☐

4 The width of a field is 16 metres. The field is being drawn on a scale diagram, using a scale of 1 cm to 2 metres. On the scale diagram, what is the width of the field? *(1 mark)*

a) 12 cm ☐ b) 16 cm ☐

c) 4 cm ☐ d) 8 cm ☐

Score / 4

B

Answer all parts of all questions.

1 The diagram shows the position of some places in a town. Decide whether each of the statements is true or false.

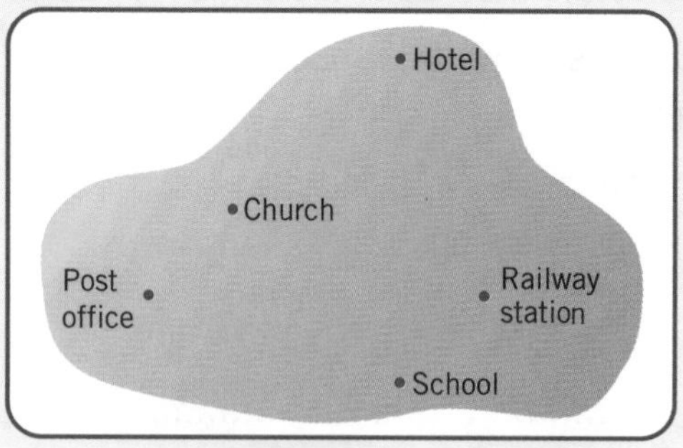

a) The post office is west of the railway station. ....

b) The hotel is on a bearing of 045° from the church. ....

c) The church is on a bearing of 225° from the post office. .... *(3 marks)*

2 Calculate the three-figure bearing of   i) B from A in each diagram   ii) A from B in each diagram.

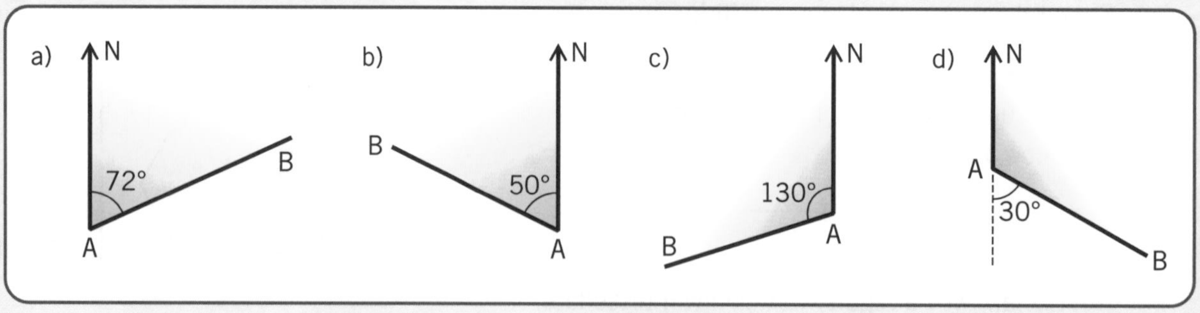

i) ....   i) ....   i) ....   i) ....

ii) ....   ii) ....   ii) ....   ii) ....

(8 marks)

3 The scale on a road map is 1 : 50 000. If two towns are 20 cm apart on the map, work out the real distance, in kilometres, between the two towns.

.... *(2 marks)*

Score / 13

54

C

These are SATs-style questions. Answer all parts of the questions.

1 Peter is making a stencil. He makes a sketch of the stencil on some paper.

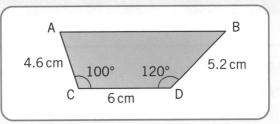

a) Make an accurate full-size drawing of the stencil in the space provided.

(4 marks)

b) Measure the length of AB to the nearest 0.1 cm. .... cm (1 mark)

2 a) The diagram shows the position of a lighthouse (L). A ship (S) is 120 km away on a bearing of 140° from the lighthouse. If 1 cm = 20 km, mark accurately on the diagram the position of the ship.

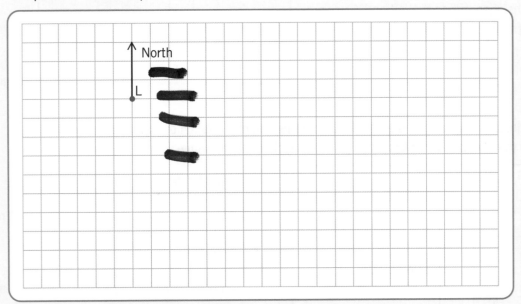

(3 marks)

b) A buoy (B) is 80 km and on a bearing of 040° from the ship. Mark accurately on the diagram the position of the buoy. (2 marks)

c) How far is the lighthouse from the buoy? .... km (1 mark)

Score   / 11

Total score   / 28

How well did you do?   ✗ 1–6 Try again   7–14 Getting there   15–22 Good work   23–28 Excellent!   ✓

For more help on this topic see KS3 Maths 3–6 Success Guide pages 54–55.

Transformations

A

Answer all parts of all questions.

1 On the grid opposite, carry out the following transformations.

a) Reflect shape A in the *y*-axis; call the shape P.

b) Reflect shape A in the *x*-axis; call the shape Q.

c) Reflect shape A in the line *x* = 4; call the shape R.

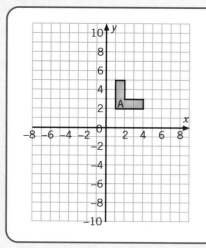

(3 marks)

2 On the grid opposite, carry out the following transformations and draw the image of the shaded shape after:

a) a reflection in the line *y* = *x*; call the image B.

b) a rotation of 180° about the origin (0, 0); call the image C.

c) a translation of 5 to the left and 4 upwards; call the image D.

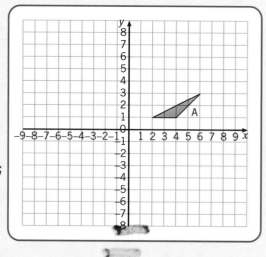

(3 marks)

3 Each of the following shapes is a translation, a reflection or a rotation of object A. State the transformation that has taken place for each of the following:

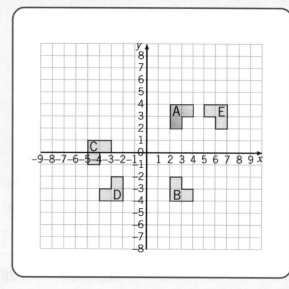

a) A is transformed to B by

.... (1 mark)

b) A is transformed to C by

.... (1 mark)

c) A is transformed to D by

.... (1 mark)

d) A is transformed to E by

.... (1 mark)

Score   / 10

These are SATs-style questions. Answer all parts of the questions.

1 Reflect triangle P in the mirror line on each of these diagrams.

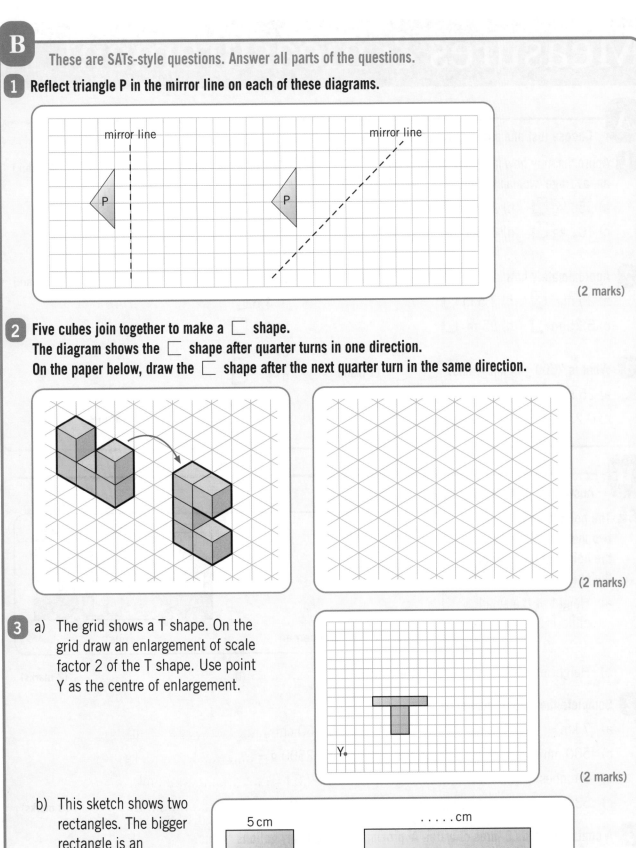

mirror line   mirror line

(2 marks)

2 Five cubes join together to make a ☐ shape.
The diagram shows the ☐ shape after quarter turns in one direction.
On the paper below, draw the ☐ shape after the next quarter turn in the same direction.

(2 marks)

3 a) The grid shows a T shape. On the grid draw an enlargement of scale factor 2 of the T shape. Use point Y as the centre of enlargement.

Y.

(2 marks)

b) This sketch shows two rectangles. The bigger rectangle is an enlargement of scale factor 3 of the smaller rectangle. Write down the two missing values.

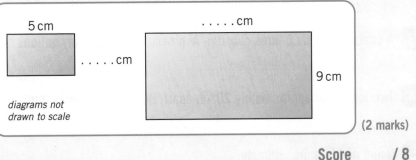

5 cm   . . . . . cm

. . . . . cm

9 cm

diagrams not drawn to scale

(2 marks)

Score   / 8

Total score   / 18

How well did you do?   ✗ 1–4 **Try again**   5–9 **Getting there**   10–14 **Good work**   15–18 **Excellent!**

For more help on this topic see KS3 Maths 3–6 Success Guide pages 56–57.

Measures & measurement 1

A

Choose just one answer, a, b, c or d.

1 Approximately how many kilograms would an 'average' woman weigh? *(1 mark)*

a) 550 kg ☐   b) 25 kg ☐

c) 102 kg ☐   d) 60 kg ☐

2 Approximately how high is a door? *(1 mark)*

a) 25 m ☐   b) 2.5 m ☐

c) 6.25 m ☐   d) 35 m ☐

3 What is 2500 g in kilograms? *(1 mark)*

a) 25 kg ☐   b) 2.5 kg ☐

c) 0.25 kg ☐   d) 250 kg ☐

4 How many millimetres are in 5.2 cm? *(1 mark)*

a) 0.52 mm ☐   b) 5200 mm ☐

c) 52 mm ☐   d) 520 mm ☐

5 Approximately how many pounds are in 3 kg? *(1 mark)*

a) 4.5 ☐

b) 6.6 ☐

c) 5.8 ☐

d) 9 ☐

Score   / 5

B

Answer all parts of all questions.

1 The policeman is almost two metres tall. Estimate the height of the bus and the child.

a) Height of the small child is approximately
.... m.

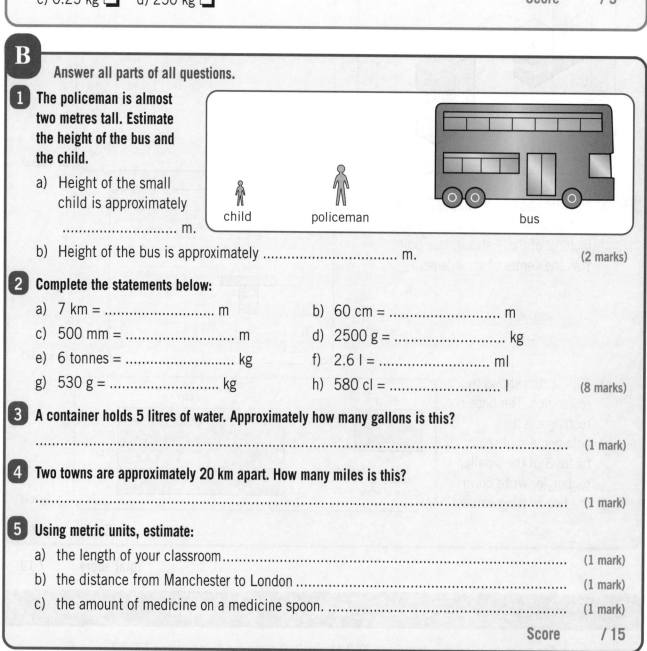

child   policeman   bus

b) Height of the bus is approximately .... m. *(2 marks)*

2 Complete the statements below:

a) 7 km = ... m

b) 60 cm = ... m

c) 500 mm = ... m

d) 2500 g = ... kg

e) 6 tonnes = ... kg

f) 2.6 l = ... ml

g) 530 g = ... kg

h) 580 cl = ... l   *(8 marks)*

3 A container holds 5 litres of water. Approximately how many gallons is this?

.... *(1 mark)*

4 Two towns are approximately 20 km apart. How many miles is this?

.... *(1 mark)*

5 Using metric units, estimate:

a) the length of your classroom.. *(1 mark)*

b) the distance from Manchester to London .... *(1 mark)*

c) the amount of medicine on a medicine spoon. .... *(1 mark)*

Score   / 15

Shape, space & measures

C

These are SATs-style questions. Answer all parts of the questions.

1 Pablo is measuring the length of a pencil.

a) How long is his pencil?...cm (1 mark)

b) A second pencil is 72 mm long.
Write the length of this pencil in centimetres ....cm (1 mark)

2 Charlotte and Reece have some sweets.

I have 50 g of sweets.

I have 3 ounces of sweets.

Who has more sweets? Explain your answer.

.... (2 marks)

3 Matthew is making a cake. He has a 5-inch bowl. Approximately how many centimetres is his bowl?

.... (1 mark)

4 A large jug holds 6 litres of liquid.

a) How many millilitres is this? ....ml (1 mark)

b) Lucy says that the jug holds approximately 4 pints of liquid.

Explain why she is wrong. ....

.... (2 marks)

Score   / 8

Total score   / 28

How well did you do?   1–6 Try again   7–11 Getting there   12–21 Good work   22–28 Excellent!

For more help on this topic see KS3 Maths 3–6 Success Guide pages 58–59.

59

Measures & measurement 2

A

Choose just one answer, a, b, c or d.

1 How many seconds are in 2 minutes? (1 mark)

a) 600 ☐ b) 60 ☐ c) 120 ☐ d) 200 ☐

2 What is 4:30 pm written in 24-hour clock time? (1 mark)

a) 1430 ☐ b) 4:30 ☐

c) 16.3 ☐ d) 1630 ☐

3 What is 1825 written in 12-hour clock time? (1 mark)

a) 6:25 pm ☐ b) 0625 ☐

c) 6:25 am ☐ d) 6:25 ☐

4 Diana leaves Rickmansworth at 12:30 pm. Her journey takes 1 hour and 18 minutes. (1 mark)

What time does Diana finish her journey?

a) 1:58 pm ☐ b) 1324 ☐

c) 1:48 pm ☐ d) 12:48 pm ☐

5 How many days are there in the month of May? (1 mark)

a) 28 ☐ b) 29 ☐ c) 30 ☐ d) 31 ☐

6 How many days are there in a leap year? (1 mark)

a) 364 ☐ b) 366 ☐ c) 365 ☐ d) 367 ☐

Score / 6

B

Answer all parts of all questions.

1 Complete the table below with the correct times.

12-hour clock	4:47 pm			2:36 pm		9:40 pm
24-hour clock		1334	1926		0217	

(2 marks)

2 Fill in these statements to make them correct.

a) There are .... seconds in a minute. (1 mark)

b) There are .... weeks in one year. (1 mark)

c) There are .... seconds in a week. (1 mark)

3 If May 19th fell on a Sunday in 2002,

a) on what day of the week did May 9th fall? .... (1 mark)

b) on what day of the week did June 9th fall? .... (1 mark)

4 The timetable illustrates the train times from Bury to Manchester.

Bury	0012	0036	Every 30 minutes until	0706	0711	Every 5 minutes until	0906
Whitefield	0020	0044		0714	0719		0914
Bowker Vale	0025	0049		0719	0724		0919
Manchester	0029	0053		0723	0728		0923

a) If Leroy sets off from Bury at 0036, how long does it take him to get to Manchester? .... (1 mark)

b) What time is the next train from Bury after the 0036 one? .... (1 mark)

c) Lily arrives at Whitefield station at 0740.
What is the time of the next train to Manchester? .... (1 mark)

Score / 10

C

These are SATs-style questions. Answer all parts of the questions.

1 Rebecca went to the gym one evening. Clock A shows the time she arrived. Clock B shows the time she left.

Clock A   Clock B

a) For how long was Rebecca at the gym?.. (1 mark)

b) Write the time she left the gym, using 24 hour clock time. .... (1 mark)

2 This shows part of the timetable for Emily's day.

8:45	Registration
9:05	History begins
9:55	History ends and Maths begins
10:45	Maths end and break begins
11:00	Break ends and Art begins
11:50	Art ends and Science begins
12:40	Science ends and lunch begins

a) How long is registration? .... (1 mark)

b) How long does the Maths lesson last?.. (1 mark)

c) A fire alarm went off at 12:13 p.m.

How many minutes was this before lunch?... (1 mark)

d) Caleb was late to school. He arrived at 10:12 a.m.

How many minutes late was he? .... (1 mark)

3 The timetable illustrates the bus times from Rickmansworth to Amersham.

Rickmansworth	0730	0750	Every 20 minutes until	0930	1030	1130
Chorleywood	0755	0813		0955	1055	1155
Little Chalfont	0802	0820		1002	1102	1202
Amersham	0810	0830		1010	1110	1210

a) Chloe sets off from Chorleywood at 0755. At what time does she arrive in Amersham?

.... (1 mark)

b) William needs to be in Little Chalfont by 10.30. What is the time of the bus that he must catch from Rickmansworth?

.... (1 mark)

Score   / 8

Total score   / 24

How well did you do?   ✗ 1–5 **Try again**   6–13 **Getting there**   14–19 **Good work**   20–24 **Excellent!** ✓

For more help on this topic see KS3 Maths 3–6 Success Guide pages 60–61.

Area & perimeter of 2D shapes

A   Answer all parts of all questions.

1 Jerry wants to put up a fence around the perimeter of his garden. The diagram shows a plan view of the garden. Calculate the length of fencing that he will need.

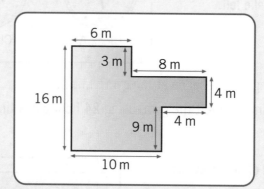

.... **(2 marks)**

2 Complete these statements.

a) The perimeter of a shape is the .... around the outside edge.

b) The area of a shape is the amount of .... that it covers.   **(2 marks)**

3 For each of these shapes calculate i) the perimeter and ii) the area.

Ⓒ

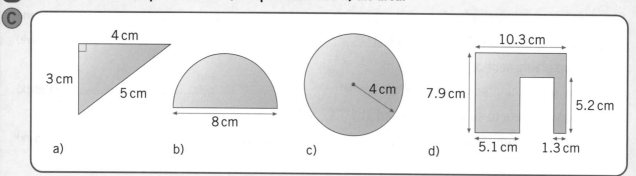

i)   perimeter: a) ....   b) ....   c) ....   d) ....

ii) area: a) ....   b) ....   c) ....   d) ....   **(8 marks)**

4 Work out the areas of these shapes. Give your answers to 1 decimal place.

Ⓒ

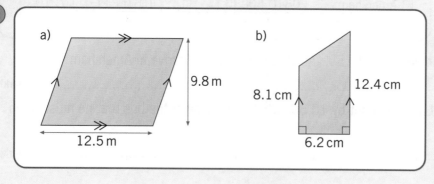

a) ....   b) ....   **(4 marks)**

Score   / 16

62   Ⓒ *Indicates that a calculator may be used*

B

These are SATs-style questions. Answer all parts of the questions.

1 Each shape in this question has an area of 20 cm².

a) Calculate the height of this rectangle.

area = 20 cm²

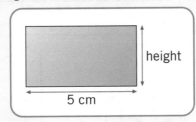

height = ... cm   (1 mark)

b) Calculate the height of this triangle.

area = 20 cm²

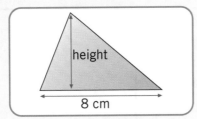

height = ... cm   (1 mark)

2 A sewing pattern is in the
C shape of a trapezium.

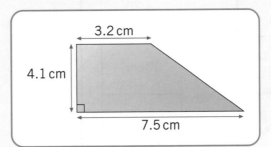

Calculate the area of the trapezium.

Show your working.

area = ... cm²   (2 marks)

3 A circle has a radius
C of 20 cm.

a) Calculate the area of the circle.

Show your working.

area = ... cm²   (2 marks)

b) A circle of radius 20 cm sits inside a
circle of radius 30 cm. Calculate the
area of the shaded region.

Show your working.

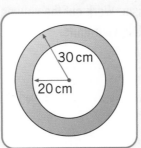

area = ... cm²   (3 marks)

Score   / 9

Total score   / 25

How well did you do?   ✗ 1–5 **Try again**   6–12 **Getting there**   13–19 **Good work**   20–25 **Excellent!**   ✓

For more help on this topic see KS3 Maths 3–6 Success Guide pages 62–63.

Volume of 3D solids

A

Answer all parts of all questions.

1 Each cube has a volume of 1 cm³.
What are the volumes of the
following shapes?

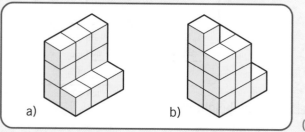

a)

b)

a) volume = ... cm³

b) volume = ... cm³

(2 marks)

2 Match each of the shapes with the correct volume.

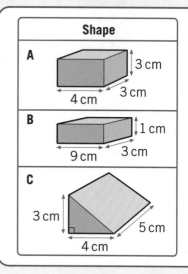

Shape	Volume
A 4 cm, 3 cm, 3 cm	27 cm³
B 9 cm, 3 cm, 1 cm	30 cm³
C 3 cm, 4 cm, 5 cm	36 cm³

(3 marks)

3 For this cuboid:

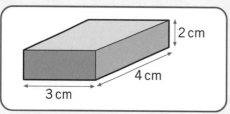

2 cm

4 cm

3 cm

a) Work out the volume. ....cm³ (1 mark)

b) Work out the total surface area. ....cm² (1 mark)

4 The diagram shows a triangular prism. Work out the volume
of the triangular prism, clearly stating your units.

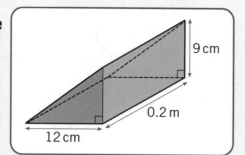

9 cm

0.2 m

12 cm

....

.... (2 marks)

5 The shape opposite is the cross-section of a prism 15 cm long.
Find the volume of the prism, clearly stating your units.

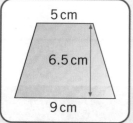

5 cm

6.5 cm

9 cm

....

.... (2 marks)

Score   / 11

64

B

These are SATs-style questions. Answer all parts of the questions.

1 In the space provided, draw a cuboid with a volume of 24 cm³.
Clearly label the lengths of each side.

(2 marks)

2 Some plates are put into a box. There are two types of boxes. If the volume of each box is the same,
C calculate the missing height of box B.

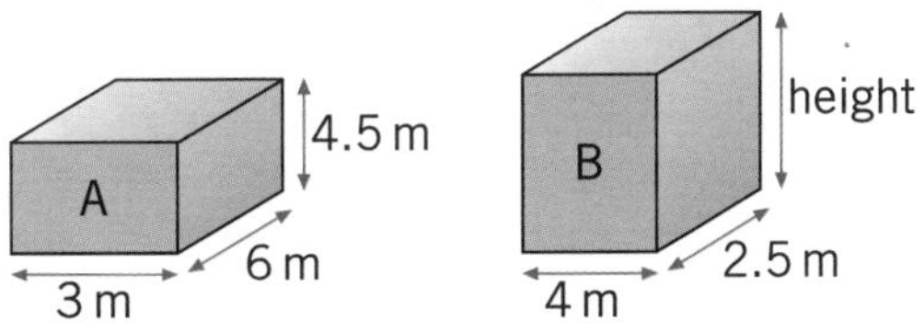

4.5 m
A
3 m   6 m

height
B
4 m   2.5 m

....cm (3 marks)

3 A piece of cheese is in the shape
C of a triangular prism.

Calculate the volume of cheese.

Show your working. ....

....

....cm³

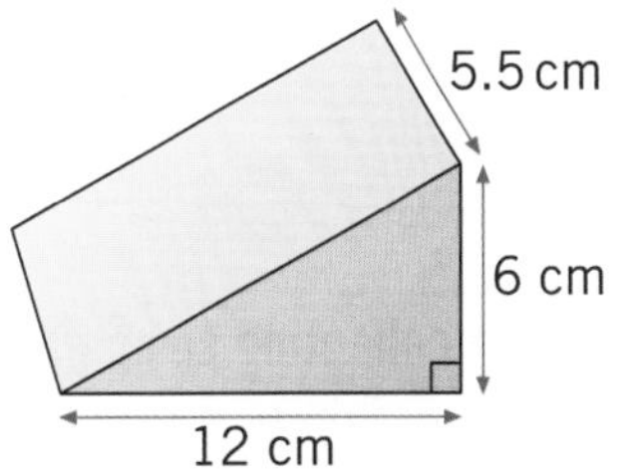

5.5 cm

6 cm

12 cm

(2 marks)

4 A container has this shape as its
C cross-section. If the container is 20 cm
deep, work out the volume.

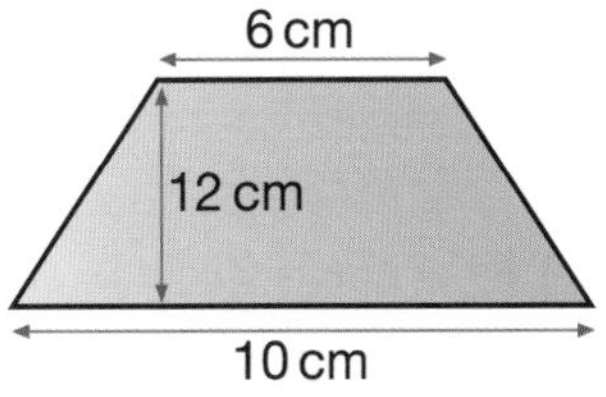

6 cm

12 cm

10 cm

Show your working. .... (2 marks)

Score   / 9

Total score   / 20

How well did you do?   ✗ 1–4 Try again   5–8 Getting there   9–14 Good work   15–20 Excellent!   ✓

For more help on this topic see KS3 Maths 3–6 Success Guide pages 64–65.

Collecting data

A

Choose just one answer, a, b, c or d.

From the frequency table given, answer the next three questions.

Weight (w kg)	Frequency
40 ⩽ w < 50	4
50 ⩽ w < 60	10
60 ⩽ w < 70	15
70 ⩽ w < 80	25
80 ⩽ w < 90	4

1 **How many people had a weight between 50 and 60 kg?** (1 mark)

a) 4 ☐   b) 10 ☐   c) 15 ☐   d) 25 ☐

2 **How many people in total were surveyed about their weight?** (1 mark)

a) 55 ☐   b) 30 ☐   c) 58 ☐   d) 60 ☐

3 **If somebody weighed 70kg, into which class interval would they go?** (1 mark)

a) 40 ⩽ w < 50 ☐   b) 50 ⩽ w < 60 ☐

c) 60 ⩽ w < 70 ☐   d) 70 ⩽ w < 80 ☐

Score   / 3

B

Answer all parts of all questions.

1 **The names of different types of data are put on cards.**

Primary data	Continuous data	Secondary data	Discrete data

Decide which of the cards goes with each of the statements below.

a) Data that somebody else has collected. .... (1 mark)

b) Data that are often found by measuring. The values change from one category to the next. .... (1 mark)

c) Data that you collect yourself. .... (1 mark)

d) Data that are often found by counting. Each category is separate. .... (1 mark)

2 **Jerry and Sam are collecting some data on eye colour for a class survey.**
Design an observation sheet that they could use.

(3 marks)

3 **The weights in kg of some students are:**

    42, 54, 61, 67, 53, 50, 48, 47, 56, 42, 44, 54, 59, 63, 73, 71, 69, 71

Complete the stem-and-leaf diagram below:

4	2 8 7 2 4
5	
6	key 4|2 means 42
7	stem = 10 kg

(2 marks)

Score   / 9

These are SATs-style questions. Answer all parts of the questions.

1 **Molly works in a book shop. She recorded the types of book she sold in one day.**
This is what she wrote down:

Crime, horror, fiction, science fiction, horror, horror, fiction, fiction, fiction, crime, horror, fiction, fiction, science fiction, crime, crime, fiction, horror, fiction, science fiction, crime, crime, fiction, fiction, horror, crime, crime, fiction, horror.

a) On a separate sheet of paper, use a tallying method to make a table showing how many books of the different types were sold during the day.

(3 marks)

b) Which type of book was the most popular?

.... (1 mark)

c) Molly said:

> Science fiction was
> the least popular.

Explain whether Molly was right.

.... (1 mark)

2 **Some pupils are doing a survey to find out the number of hours their friends spent watching television in a week. They wrote a questionnaire.**

a) One question was:

How old are you (in years)?

10 or younger	10 to 15	15 to 20	20 to 25	25 or older

Explain why the labels for the middle three boxes need to be changed.

.... (2 marks)

b) Another question was:

How long do you spend watching television in a week?

☐ don't know   ☐ none   ☐ a small amount   ☐ lots

Rhysian said that the labels need changing.

Write new labels for the boxes. You may change as many boxes as you want.

.... (2 marks)

Score   / 9

Total score   / 21

How well did you do?   ✗ 1–4 **Try again**   5–9 **Getting there**   10–15 **Good work**   16–21 **Excellent!** ✓

For more help on this topic see KS3 Maths 3–6 Success Guide pages 68–69.

67

Representing information

A Answer all parts of all questions.

1 Mr Young is conducting a survey on the types of house that some students live in. His findings are shown in this pictogram.

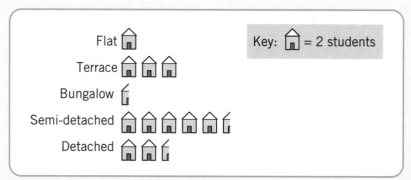

Key: 🏠 = 2 students

Flat
Terrace
Bungalow
Semi-detached
Detached

Based on the information given in the pictogram, decide whether these statements are true or false.

a) The majority of students live in semi-detached houses. .... (1 mark)

b) Six students live in flats... (1 mark)

c) Five students live in detached houses.. (1 mark)

d) One person lives in a bungalow. .... (1 mark)

e) Using the scale below, draw the information shown in the pictogram as a bar chart.

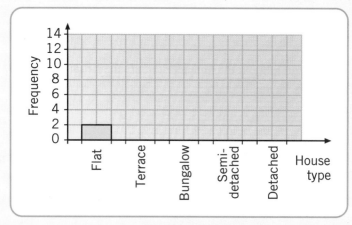

(2 marks)

2 The pie chart shows how Erin spends a typical day.

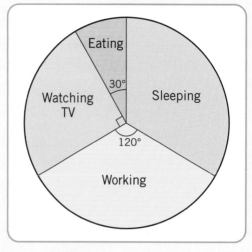

a) Measure the size of the angle for sleeping...

b) Work out the number of hours that Erin works. ....

c) For how many hours does Erin watch TV?... (3 marks)

Score   / 9

Ⓒ *Indicates that a calculator may be used*

These are SATs-style questions. Answer all parts of the questions.

1 The frequency table and chart show how long (in minutes) 30 people spent queuing at a supermarket checkout.

Time (t minutes)	Frequency
$0 \leqslant t < 5$	12
$5 \leqslant t < 10$	....
$10 \leqslant t < 15$	....
$15 \leqslant t < 20$	4
$20 \leqslant t < 25$	1

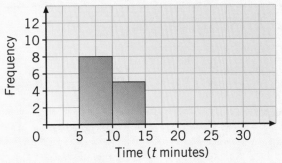

a) Use the information in the frequency table to complete the frequency diagram. (2 marks)

b) Use the information in the frequency diagram to complete the frequency table. (2 marks)

c) Rameen says:

Most people queue for less than 10 minutes

Explain whether he is right. .... (1 mark)

2 A teacher asked her class:

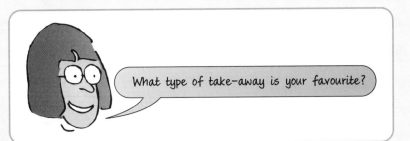

What type of take-away is your favourite?

a) The results from her class are shown in the table below:

Type of take-away	Frequency
Indian	11
Chinese	4
Pizza	8
Fried chicken	1

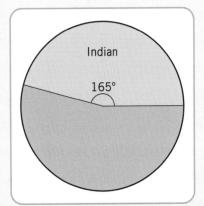

Indian

165°

Complete the pie chart to show this information. Show your working and draw your angles accurately.

(2 marks)

b) What fraction of the class likes pizza best? .... (1 marks)

Score / 8

Total score / 17

How well did you do?   ✗ 1–3 **Try again**   4–7 **Getting there**   8–13 **Good work**   14–17 **Excellent!** ✓

For more help on this topic see KS3 Maths 3–6 Success Guide pages 70–71.

69

REPRESENTING INFORMATION

Handling data

Scatter diagrams & misleading graphs

A

Answer all parts of all questions.

1

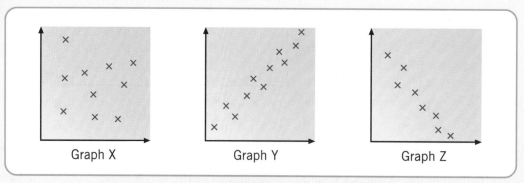

Graph X   Graph Y   Graph Z

Which of the graphs above best illustrates the relationship between:

a) the weight of children and their mark in a maths test?   Graph .... (1 mark)

b) the age of a car and its value?   Graph .... (1 mark)

c) the age of a car and its mileage?   Graph .... (1 mark)

d) rising temperatures and the sales of ice cream?   Graph .... (1 mark)

e) rising temperatures and the sales of woollen hats?   Graph .... (1 mark)

2 **In a survey, the heights of ten girls and their shoe sizes were measured.**

Height in cm	150	157	159	161	158	164	154	152	162	168
Shoe size	3	5	$5\frac{1}{2}$	6	5	$6\frac{1}{2}$	4	$3\frac{1}{2}$	6	7

a) Draw a scatter diagram showing these data.

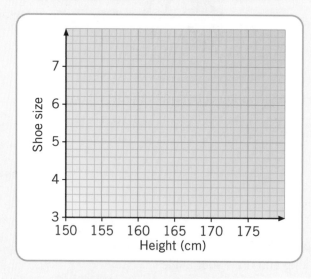

(2 marks)

b) What type of correlation is there between height and shoe size?

.... (1 mark)

c) From your scatter diagram, estimate the height of a girl whose shoe size is $4\frac{1}{2}$.

.... (1 mark)

Score   / 9

These are SATs-style questions. Answer all parts of the questions.

1 **The graph shows the sales of a washing powder over a period of 4 months.**

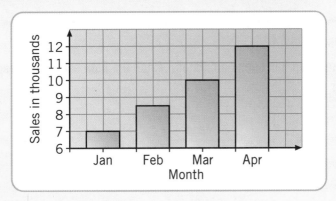

Explain why this graph is misleading. .... (2 marks)

2 **Some students did a survey of how well they did in a maths test compared to the hours they spent revising and the hours spent watching television. They plotted their results as scatter diagrams.**

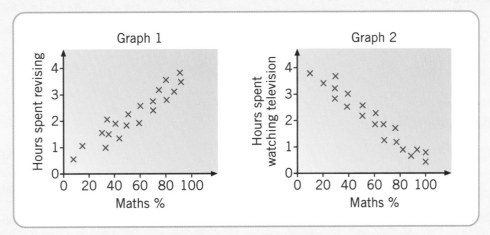

a) What does Graph 1 show about the relationship between the maths percentage and the hours spent revising?

.... (1 mark)

b) What does Graph 2 show about the relationship between the maths percentage and the hours spent watching television?

.... (1 mark)

c) If a scatter diagram was drawn to show the relationship between the students' maths percentage and their height, what type of correlation would it show?

.... (1 mark)

d) Another student spent 3 hours revising. Using Graph 1, estimate the student's maths score.

.... (1 mark)

Score   / 6

Total score   / 15

How well did you do?   ✗ 1–3 **Try again**   4–7 **Getting there**   8–11 **Good work**   12–15 **Excellent!**   ✓

For more help on this topic see KS3 Maths 3–6 Success Guide pages 72–73.

Averages 1

A

Answer all parts of all questions.

1 For each set of numbers the mean has been calculated. Match the data with the correct mean. The first has been done for you.

Data	Mean
1, 2, 3, 4, 5	6
1.4, 2.8, 3.1, 4.2, 5.6	29.8
9, 21, 30, 38, 51	3
10, 20, 30, 40, 50	3.42
2, 4, 6, 8, 10	30

(4 marks)

2 Here are some number cards:

2 7 3 6 2 2 1 3 4 2

For these number cards, calculate:

a) the mean .... (1 mark)

b) the median .... (1 mark)

c) the mode .... (1 mark)

d) the range .... (1 mark)

3 The mean length of 10 tadpoles is 3.2 cm. What is the total length of the tadpoles in centimetres?

.... (1 mark)

4 Jessie finds the median of some cards:

7 2 9 4 10

She says that '9 is the median'. Explain why she is wrong.

.... (2 marks)

Score   / 11

 Indicates that a calculator may be used

B These are SATs-style questions. Answer all parts of the questions.

1 Ellie has these four number cards:

The mean is 4.

a) What is the range of the numbers? .... (1 mark)

b) Ellie takes another card:

The mean of the five cards is now 5.

i) What number is on her new card? .... (1 mark)

ii) What is the range of her cards now? .... (1 mark)

iii) What is the mode of her five cards? .... (1 mark)

c) Thomas has these four number cards:

i) What is the mean of his four cards? .... (2 marks)

Thomas takes another card.

The mean goes up by 1.

ii) What number is on his new card? .... (2 marks)

2 There are three hidden cards:

The mode of the three numbers is 7.
The mean of the three numbers is 9.
What are the three numbers? .... (3 marks)

Score   / 11

Total score   / 22

How well did you do?   ✗ 1–5 **Try again**   6–12 **Getting there**   13–17 **Good work**   18–22 **Excellent!** ✓

For more help on this topic see KS3 Maths 3–6 Success Guide pages 74–75.

73

Averages 2

A

Choose just one answer, a, b, c or d.

The following questions are based on the data given in the table below.

The weights of some potatoes:

Weight (*W* g)	Frequency
$20 \leqslant W < 30$	5
$30 \leqslant W < 40$	6
$40 \leqslant W < 50$	4
$50 \leqslant W < 60$	5

1 How many potatoes weighed less then 50 g? (1 mark)

a) 15 ☐   b) 5 ☐   c) 6 ☐   d) 20 ☐

2 Which of the class intervals is the modal class? (1 mark)

a) $20 \leqslant W < 30$ ☐   b) $30 \leqslant W < 40$ ☐

c) $40 \leqslant W < 50$ ☐   d) $50 \leqslant W < 60$ ☐

3 C A die is thrown and the scores are noted. The results are shown in the table below. What is the mean die score? (1 mark)

Die score	1	2	3	4	5	6
Frequency	12	15	10	8	14	13

a) 5 ☐   b) 3 ☐   c) 4 ☐   d) 3.5 ☐

4 Using the information in the table above, what is the modal score? (1 mark)

a) 15 ☐

b) 2 ☐

c) 4 ☐

d) 8 ☐

Score   / 4

B

Answer all parts of all questions.

1 C The Light Away match company claims that, 'On average, a box of matches contains 48 matches.' In order to check the accuracy of this claim, a sample of 50 boxes was taken and the number of matches in each box counted. The results are given in the table below.

Number of matches	45	46	47	48	49	50
Frequency	4	5	10	20	8	3

a) Find the mean number of matches per box. .... (2 marks)

b) Explain briefly whether you think the manufacturer is justified in making its claim.

.... (1 mark)

2 Two classes have their heights measured. The mean height and the range for both classes are written in the table below.

	Mean height	Range
Class A	152 cm	5 cm
Class B	167 cm	42 cm

Matthew says that, 'All of class B are taller than class A.' Explain whether Matthew is correct.

.... (2 marks)

Score   / 5

74

 Indicates that a calculator may be used

C These are SATs-style questions. Answer all parts of the questions.

1 The frequency table shows the scores obtained by some students when doing a mental arithmetic test.

C

Score	25	26	27	28	29	30
Frequency	3	10	20	10	2	5

a) How many students scored fewer than 28 marks in the mental arithmetic test?

.... (1 mark)

b) Work out the mean score on the test. Show your working.

Mean = ... (3 marks)

c) What is the modal score for the test?

Modal score = ... (1 mark)

2 In a Saturday league football tournament, the numbers of goals scored are shown in the table below.

C

Number of goals scored	0	1	2	3	4	5
Frequency	5	8	9	3	3	2

a) Work out the mean number of goals scored in the tournament.

Mean = ... (2 marks)

b) Work out the mode and the median.

Mode = ... (2 marks)

Median = ... (2 marks)

3 Mr Robinson is going to purchase some nails. Two companies give him the following data about the length of their nails.

Company A	Company B
Mean = 25 mm Range = 8 mm	Mean = 25 mm Range = 1.3 mm

From which company should he purchase the nails?

Explain your reasoning.

.... (2 marks)

Score   / 13

Total score   / 22

How well did you do? ✗ 1–6 **Try again**   7–11 **Getting there**   12–17 **Good work**   18–22 **Excellent!** ✓

For more help on this topic see KS3 Maths 3–6 Success Guide pages 76–77.

75

Probability 1

A

Answer all parts of all questions.

1 Match one of these words to each statement.

| Impossible | Certain | Evens chance | Likely | Unlikely |

a) I will wake up in the morning with seven heads. .... (1 mark)

b) I will get 'tails' when I throw a fair coin. .... (1 mark)

c) I will be older next week than I am today. .... (1 mark)

d) I will watch television this week. .... (1 mark)

e) I will have no homework this week. .... (1 mark)

2 A bag contains 3 red, 4 blue and 6 green balls. If a ball is chosen at random from the bag, what is the probability of choosing:

a) a red ball .... (1 mark)

b) a green ball .... (1 mark)

c) a yellow ball .... (1 mark)

d) a blue or a red ball. .... (1 mark)

3 A box of chocolates contains 15 hard centres and 13 soft centres. One chocolate is chosen at random. Work out the probability that it will be:

a) a hard centre .... (1 mark)

b) a soft centre .... (1 mark)

c) a biscuit. .... (1 mark)

4 Rupinder spins the spinner shown opposite.
She says: 'The probability of me getting a 3 is $\frac{1}{3}$.'

a) Explain why she is wrong.

.... (1 mark)

b) What is the probability of obtaining a 3?

.... (1 mark)

5 Decide whether each of these statements is true or false.

a) If the probability that I receive a letter is 72%, the probability that I do not receive a letter is 28%. .... (1 mark)

b) The probability that a flag is not coloured red is 0.26. The probability that a flag is coloured red is 0.64. .... (1 mark)

c) The probability that the 'Go Aheads' win a darts match is $\frac{41}{63}$.
The probability that they do not win a darts match is $\frac{20}{63}$ .... (1 mark)

Score / 17

These are SATs-style questions. Answer all parts of the questions.

1 **A bag contains 3 yellow beads and 2 red beads.**

a) Lucy is going to take a bead out of the bag at random.

She says:

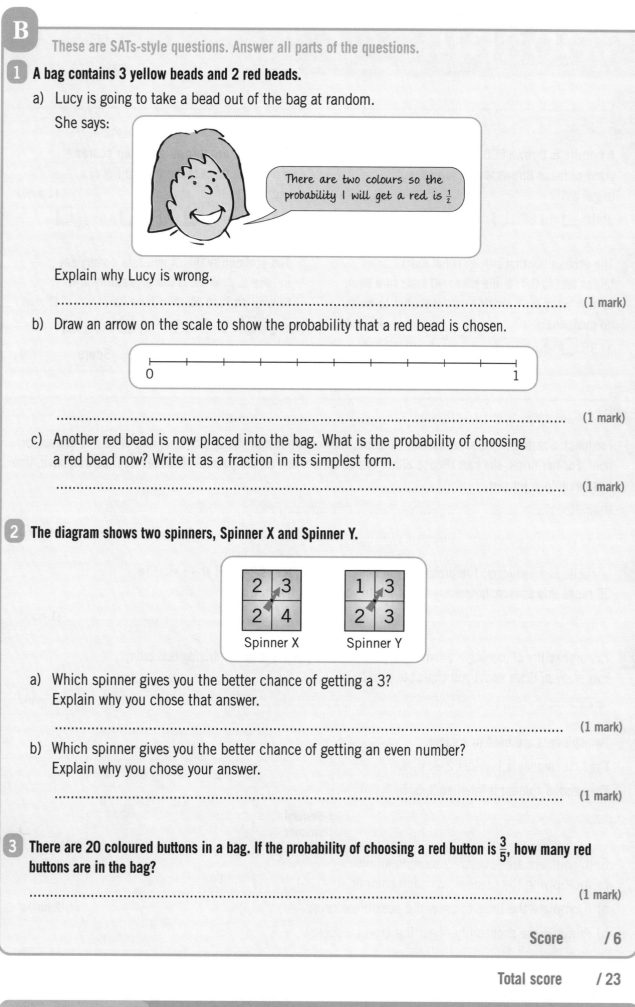

There are two colours so the probability I will get a red is $\frac{1}{2}$

Explain why Lucy is wrong.

.... (1 mark)

b) Draw an arrow on the scale to show the probability that a red bead is chosen.

0 |—|—|—|—|—|—|—|—|—|—| 1

.... (1 mark)

c) Another red bead is now placed into the bag. What is the probability of choosing a red bead now? Write it as a fraction in its simplest form.

.... (1 mark)

2 **The diagram shows two spinners, Spinner X and Spinner Y.**

| 2 | 3 |
| 2 | 4 |
Spinner X

| 1 | 3 |
| 2 | 3 |
Spinner Y

a) Which spinner gives you the better chance of getting a 3?
Explain why you chose that answer.

.... (1 mark)

b) Which spinner gives you the better chance of getting an even number?
Explain why you chose your answer.

.... (1 mark)

3 **There are 20 coloured buttons in a bag. If the probability of choosing a red button is $\frac{3}{5}$, how many red buttons are in the bag?**

.... (1 mark)

Score   / 6

Total score   / 23

How well did you do?   ✗ 1–5 **Try again**   6–11 **Getting there**   12–18 **Good work**   19–23 **Excellent!** ✓

For more help on this topic see KS3 Maths 3–6 Success Guide pages 78–79.

77

PROBABILITY 1   Handling data

Probability 2

A

Choose just one answer, a, b, c or d.

1 A fair die is thrown 600 times. On how many of these throws would you expect to get a 4? **(1 mark)**

a) 40 ☐ b) 600 ☐ c) 100 ☐ d) 580 ☐

2 The probability that Lilly gets full marks in a tables test is 0.7. If she takes 40 tests in a year, in how many tests would you expect her to make no mistakes? **(1 mark)**

a) 35 ☐ b) 28 ☐ c) 30 ☐ d) 18 ☐

3 If two dice are thrown and their scores are added, what is the probability of a score of 12? **(1 mark)**

a) $\frac{1}{2}$ ☐ b) $\frac{2}{12}$ ☐ c) $\frac{1}{36}$ ☐ d) $\frac{2}{36}$ ☐

4 The probability that it will rain on any day in June is $\frac{2}{9}$. What is the probability of it raining on June 5th and June 9th? **(1 mark)**

a) $\frac{4}{81}$ ☐ b) $\frac{4}{18}$ ☐ c) $\frac{4}{9}$ ☐ d) $\frac{2}{9}$ ☐

Score   / 4   2

B

Answer all parts of all questions.

1 For lunch Scarlett has a sandwich and a drink. For her sandwich, she can choose one of ham or cheese or beef. For her drink, she can choose either tea or coffee. List all the possible lunches Scarlett can have. One has been done for you.

(ham, tea) ....

.... **(2 marks)**   2

2 Michelle is a swimmer. The probability of her winning a race is 84%. If she swims in 50 races this season, how many races would you expect her to win?

.... **(1 mark)**   1

3 The probability of passing a driving test is 0.7. If 200 people take the driving test today, how many of them would you expect to pass?

.... **(1 mark)**   1

4 Two spinners are used in a game.

The first spinner is labelled 2, 4, 6, 8.

The second spinner is labelled 3, 5, 5, 7.

		First spinner			
		2	**4**	**6**	**8**
Second spinner	**3**	6	12	18	24
	5	10			
	5	10			
	7	14			

Both spinners are spun. The score is found by multiplying the numbers on each spinner.

a) Complete the table to show the possible scores. **(2 marks)**   2

b) What is the probability of getting an even score?

.... **(1 mark)**

c) What is the probability of getting a score of 10?

.... **(1 mark)**

Score   / 8

78

Ⓒ *Indicates that a calculator may be used*

These are SATs-style questions. Answer all parts of the questions.

1 **A scratch card has the following boxes:**
To win a prize you must choose the
correct combination.

You need to choose one of the letters and
one of the numbers, for example, M1.

K ○	L ○	M ○
1 ⬜	2 ⬜	
3 ⬜	4 ⬜	
5 ⬜	6 ⬜	

a) How many different combinations can you choose?
Show all combinations.

....

.... (2 marks)

b) The prize always occurs with the number 5. If I scratch off the 5, what is the
probability of winning?

.... (1 mark)

2 **Melissa is a keen athlete. She estimates that the probability she wins each race is 0.3.**
If she runs 20 races, how many of these races would she expect to win?

.... (1 mark)

3 **Hywel and Tracey are playing a game. They each have 4 cards.**

1	3	5	7		1	2	3	4

Hywel's cards   Tracey's cards

They each take any one of their own cards. They then multiply the numbers on the two cards.
The table shows all the possible results.

×	1	3	5	7
1	1	3	5	7
2	2	6	10	14
3	3	9	15	21
4	4	12	20	28

a) What is the probability that their answer is a multiple of 3? .... (1 mark)

b) What is the probability that their answer is less than 12? .... (1 mark)

Score   / 6

Total score   / 18

How well did you do?   ✗ 1–4 **Try again**   5–9 **Getting there**   10–14 **Good work**   15–18 **Excellent!** ✓

SATS exam practice

Non-calculator questions   Levels 3–6

1 How much of each rectangular grid is shaded?

Tick (✓) the correct box.

a)

More than half ☐

Half ☐

Less than half ☐

b)

More than half ☐

Half ☐

Less than half ☐

c)

More than half ☐

Half ☐

Less than half ☐

(3 marks)

2 a) Add together **214** and **329**.. (1 mark)

b) Subtract **147** from **629**. .... (1 mark)

c) Multiply **75** by **6**.. (1 mark)

d) Divide **273** by **3**.. (1 mark)

3 Richard and Nigel do a survey together.

Richard draws a pictogram.

Holiday destination

Greece   ◯ ◯ ◯ ◯ ◯

France   ◯ ◯ ◖

Portugal ◯ ◯ ◯ ◯

USA   ◯ ◖

Key: ◯ = 2 people

Nigel shows the same information but draws a bar chart.

Complete Nigel's bar chart.

(2 marks)

4 Two pupils drew some angles on squared paper:

Angle P   Angle R

a) Which word best describes angle P?

Tick the correct box.

Acute ☐   Obtuse ☐

Right-angle ☐ Reflex ☐

(1 mark)

b) Estimate the size of angle R.

Estimate .... degrees (1 mark)

5

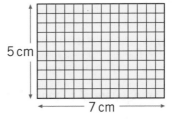

Special offer:
3 kg oranges for £2.84

How much would it cost to buy 15 kg of oranges?
Show your working.

£ .... (2 marks)

6 Bonnie has some cards:

| 6 | 7 | 8 | 9 | . | 5 | 1 | 3 |

She makes the number 6.78 with four of her cards.

a) Use some of the cards to make the number **10 times** bigger than 6.78. .... (1 mark)

b) Use some of the cards to make the number which is **100 times** bigger than 6.78. .... (1 mark)

c) Use some of the cards to make the number which is **double** 6.78............................... (1 mark)

d) Which of the numbers on the cards are prime numbers? .... (1 mark)

7 The diagram shows a box with no lid.
Complete the net for the box.

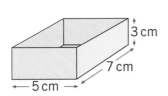

3 cm
7 cm
5 cm

5 cm
7 cm

(2 marks)

8 Patrick and Frances are
playing a game using the
two boards shown opposite:

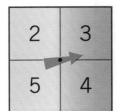

| 2 | 3 |
| 5 | 4 |

5 2
1

In one 'go', both spinners are turned. The score for the 'go' is the two numbers **multiplied** together.

a) Complete the table to show all the possible scores for one 'go'. (1 mark)

		Square spinner			
		2	**3**	**4**	**5**
	1		3		
Triangle spinner	**2**				
	5				25

b) What is the **probability** that the score is an **odd** number?

.... (1 mark)

c) What is the **probability** that the score is a **square** number?

.... (1 mark)

d) Complete the sentence below:

The probability that the score is less than .... is **zero**. (1 mark)

e) What is the probability that the score is **greater than 10**?

.... (1 mark)

9 a) When $x = 3$, work out the values of the expressions below.

i) $4x + 3$ ....

ii) $3x - 4$ ....

iii) $5 + 2x$ .... (2 marks)

b) When $3n + 4 = 28$, work out the value of n.

Show your working. $n =$ .... (2 marks)

c) Solve the equation.

$7y - 3 = 3y + 9$

Show your working. $y =$ .... (2 marks)

10 The diagram shows an equilateral triangle and an isosceles triangle inside a rectangle.

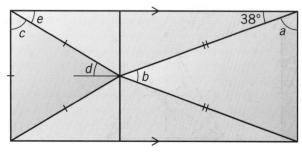

Calculate the sizes of the missing angles.

$a =$ ....

$b =$ ....

$c =$ ....

$d =$ ....

$e =$ ....

(5 marks)

Total / 35

SATS exam practice

Calculator questions   Levels 3–6

1 Colin and Gill are playing a game.

a) Gill has three hundred and twenty-seven points.

Write this number in figures.

.... (1 mark)

b) Colin has seven hundred and three points.

Write this number in figures.

.... (1 mark)

c) The game finishes when Colin gets to one thousand three hundred points.

How many more points does Colin need to finish the game?

.... (1 mark)

2 a) On the scale below, what number   The number is .... (1 mark)
is the arrow pointing to?

b) On the scale below, draw an arrow to show the number 43.

(1 mark)

3 a) A shape has 4 straight sides.

It has 4 right angles.

All the 4 sides are the same length.

Draw what the shape could be.

(1 mark)

b) A shape has 4 straight sides.

It has no right angles.

It has 1 pair of parallel sides.

Draw what the shape could be.

(1 mark)

83

4 I throw a fair die.

For each statement below, put a tick (✓)
to show if the statement is true or false.

a) On each throw, the probability of getting a six is $\frac{1}{6}$.

True ☐   False ☐

Explain your answer. .... (1 mark)

b) In six throws, it is certain that I will get one of each number.

True ☐   False ☐

Explain your answer. .... (1 mark)

5 Calculate:

a) 5% of 48.50 = ...

b) $17\frac{1}{2}$% of £60 = ...

c) $\frac{1}{8}$ of £420 = ... (3 marks)

6 The perimeter of this shape is $3 + 2t$.

a) Write an expression for the perimeter (p) of each of the following shapes.
Write each expression in its simplest form.

i)

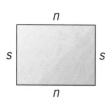

p = ... (1 mark)

ii)

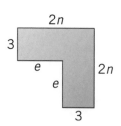

p = ... (1 mark)

iii)

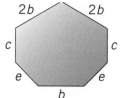

p = ... (1 mark)

b) If the perimeter of the rectangle below is 20 cm, calculate the value of y.

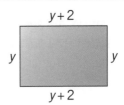

$y =$ .... (1 mark)

7 Miss Taylor decided to organise some end-of-term trips for her class.
She carried out a survey of favourite activities and put the results into the table below.

	Skating	Cinema	Boat trip	Bowling
Number of pupils	3	6	12	9

a) What percentage of the pupils wanted to go to the cinema?   ....% (1 mark)

b) What fraction of the pupils wanted to go on the boat trip?

Write the fraction in its simplest form... (1 mark)

c) Miss Taylor found out that the boat trip was too expensive. Out of the 12 pupils who wanted to go on the boat trip, 75% of them decided to go to the cinema instead, whilst the remaining pupils decided to go bowling.

Complete the table below showing the number of pupils now going on each trip.

	Skating	Cinema	Bowling
Number of pupils	3	....	....

(2 marks)

d) Complete the line below to show the ratios of pupils going on each trip.

Skating : Cinema : Bowling

1   : .... : ....   (2 marks)

e) On the day of the trip, one of the pupils was ill and could not go.
What is the probability that this pupil was supposed to go skating?

.... (1 mark)

8 A teacher has a pile of cards.

An expression for the total number of cards is $8n + 10$.

a) The teacher makes two equal piles:

Write an expression to show the number of cards in each pile.

.... (1 mark)

b) The teacher puts all the cards together again, then she uses them to make three piles.
There are 16 cards in the first pile.

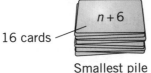 16 cards
Smallest pile $n + 6$

Biggest pile $4n + 2$

Second biggest pile $3n + 2$

How many cards are there in the third pile? .... (2 marks)

9 The scatter diagram shows the ages of some cars and how much they are worth.

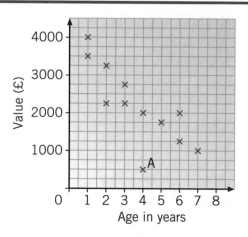

a) What does the graph show about the relationship between the age of the car and its value?

.... (1 mark)

b) Philip's car is 2 years old. Use the graph to estimate its value.   Value = ... (1 mark)

c) Car A is 4 years old but only worth £500. Explain why you think it is not worth very much.

....

.... (1 mark)

d) Jacqueline paid £1500 for her car. Approximately how old is it?   .... years   (1 mark)

10 The diagram shows the graph of the straight line $y = 2x$.

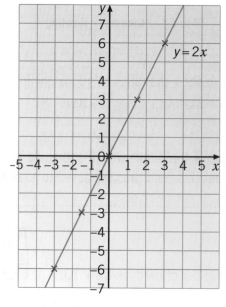

a) Draw the graph of the straight line $y = 2x - 1$ on the grid above. (1 mark)

b) Draw the graph of the straight line $y = 2x + 1$ on the grid above. (1 mark)

c) All three graphs are parallel. Explain which part of the equation helps you decide whether they are parallel or not.

.... (1 mark)

d) Write down the equation of another line which is parallel to $y = 2x$. $y =$ .... (1 mark)

e) $y = 2x$ goes through (0, 0), $y = 2x - 1$ goes through (0, –1) and $y = 2x + 1$ goes through (0, 1). Which part of the equation helps you see where the line crosses the y-axis?

.... (1 mark)

f) Where would the line $y = 2x - 10$ cross the y-axis? (......................, ...) (1 mark)

Total   / 36

Mental arithmetic test

**For this first group of questions you will have
5 seconds to work out each answer and write it down.**

1. Look at the numbers on your answer sheet. Add them up.

2. How many minutes are between three o'clock and ten past four?

3. A pen costs eleven pence. What is the total cost of seven pens?

4. How many faces does a cuboid have?

5. What is the sum of the angles in a quadrilateral?

6. When *a* equals 2, what is the value of 7*a*?

7. Multiply zero point six by ten.

8. Write down the number that is seven greater than minus three.

**For this next group of questions you will have
10 seconds to work out each answer and write it down.**

9. Write the ratio fifteen to six in its simplest form.

10. How many metres are in three and a half kilometres?

11. How many seconds are there in three minutes?

12. What is the next number in this doubling sequence? Two, four, eight ...

13. Look at the answer sheet. What is the name of this shape?

14. Twenty-five per cent of a number is seven. What is the number?

15. Double sixty-nine.

16. Look at the equation on the answer sheet. If *p* equals six, what is *n*?

17. What number is the arrow pointing to on the number line?

18. Work out the size of the missing angle in the triangle.

19. Look at the expression on your answer sheet. Simplify it.

20. What is the total cost of four books at two pounds and ninety-nine pence each?

21. What is one-eighth of sixty-four pounds?

22. If *a* = 2 and *b* = 3, work out the value of the expression on the answer sheet.

23. What is twenty per cent of four hundred pounds?

24. A bag contains three red and four blue beads. A bead is chosen at random from the bag. Write down the probability of choosing a red bead.

**For this next group of questions you will have
15 seconds to work out each answer and write it down.**

25. Which of the nets on your answer sheet will fold to make a square-based pyramid? Put a circle around the correct net.

26. Look at the pie chart on the answer sheet, which shows how five hundred and forty children spent Saturday night. How many children went to the cinema?

27. The diagram shows a square. Its perimeter is 24 centimetres. What is the area of the square?

28. Look at the numbers on your answer sheet. These are the ages of four children. Work out the mean age of the children

29. Look at the map on your answer sheet. The scale is one centimetre to ten kilometres. Estimate how many kilometres it is by road from town A to town B.

30. I am thinking of two numbers that add up to fifteen. One of my numbers is four times the size of the other. What are my two numbers?

Name:

Class:

Total marks

Time: 5 seconds

1 [ ] [ ]   7, 8, 25

2 [minutes] [ ]

3 [pence] [ ]   11 pence

4 [faces] [ ]

5 [degrees] [ ]

6 [ ] [ ] $a = 2$, $7a$

7 [ ] [ ]   0.6

8 [ ] [ ]   −3

Time: 10 seconds

9 [ ] [ ]   15 : 6

10 [metres] [ ]   3.5 km

11 [seconds] [ ]   3 minutes

12 [ ] [ ]   2, 4, 8

13 [ ] [ ]

14 [ ] [ ]

15 [ ] [ ]   69

16 [ ] [ ] $n = 2p + 1$

17 [ ] [ ]

18 [degrees] [ ]   110° a 40°

19 [ ] [ ] $5a + 3a + 2b$

20 [ ] [ ]   £2.99

21 [£] [ ]   £64

22 [ ] [ ] $2a + b$

23 [£] [ ]   £400

24 [ ] [ ]   3 red
4 blue

Time: 15 seconds

25 [ ] [ ]   A B C D

26 [children] [ ]   Bowling 180° 60° 75° 45° Cinema Disco Ice rink

27 [cm²] [ ]   perimeter 24 cm

28 [mean age =] [ ]   2, 5, 7, 10

29 [km] [ ]   A C B

30 [and] [ ]